FEDERAL POPULATION CENSUS, 1910

A catalog of microfilm copies of the schedules available through the Census Microfilm Rental Program

Census Microfilm Rental Program
Post Office Box 30
Annapolis Junction, MD 20701-0030

September 1988

Foreword

The film identified for rental in this catalogue is the same National Archives 1910 Census film that was recently made available for public release. It represents the initial offering of this data to the public on a nationwide basis.

The film identification numbers shown in this catalogue are identical to those in the companion National Archives catalogue. Either catalogue may be used to identify film for rental under this program.

Introduction

This catalog lists the 1910 population census schedules (reproduced as microfilm publication T624) and the 1910 Soundex/Miracode system (reproduced as a separate microfilm publication for Alabama, Arkansas, California, Florida, Georgia, Illinois, Kansas, Kentucky, Louisiana, Michigan, Mississippi, Missouri, North Carolina, Ohio, Oklahoma, Pennsylvania, South Carolina, Tennessee, Texas, Virginia and West Virginia). The census schedules are arranged by State or Territory and thereunder by county. For a guide to the Soundex/Miracode system, see appendix I of this catalog.

This catalog supplements the *Federal Population Censuses, 1790-1890* and the *1900 Federal Population Census* catalogs, which contain details for ordering copies of the original population schedules for 1790-1900 and of the 1880 Soundex and 1900 Soundex. Requests for these catalogs should be directed to the Census Microfilm Rental Program, P.O. Box 2940, Hyattsville, MD 20784.

The 1910 Census Schedules

The 1910 census schedules record the following information for each person: name; relationship to head of household; sex; color or race; age at last birthday; marital status; length of present marriage; if a mother, number of children and number of living children; place of birth; place of birth of parents; if foreign born, year of immigration and citizenship status; language spoken; occupation; type of industry employed in; if employer, employee, or self-employed; if unemployed; number of weeks unemployed in 1909; ability to read and write; if attended daytime school since Sept. 1, 1909; if home is rented or owned; if home is owned, free or mortaged; if home is a house or a farm; if a survivor of the Union or Confederate Army or Navy; if blind in both eyes; and if deaf and dumb. The forms used to survey Indians recorded also the tribe and/or band.

1910 Soundex/Miracode

Indexes (Soundex and Miracode) were created by the Bureau of the Census for 21 States. With the exception of Louisiana, which uses both, each State is indexed with either Soundex or Miracode as noted at the beginning of the State listing. The Soundex/Miracode for each of the 21 States has been filmed by the National Archives on a separate microfilm publication. Both the Soundex and Miracode contain the following information on cards: surname, first name, State and county of residence, city (if appropriate), race, age, and place of birth. Each card also lists the volume number and enumeration district number of the census schedule from which the information was obtained. A Miracode card lists the visitation number assigned by the enumerator, while a Soundex card shows the page and line numbers on the appropriate census schedule. The letter at the beginning of the Soundex code is the first letter of the surname of the individual; the number is a phonetic code for the surname, followed by the first name. A guide to the use of the Soundex system, which is the same for *both* the Soundex and Miracode cards, is found in appendix I of this catalog. Appendix II of this catalog contains a list of relationship terms and abbreviations used on the Soundex/Miracode cards.

Enumeration Districts

This catalog is arranged by State and thereunder by county. Persons wishing to consult the schedules for a particular town, a minor civil division or geographic area, or a ward of a large city need to know the enumeration district numbers assigned to that designated place.

Rolls 28 through 40 of microfilm publication T1224, *Census Enumeration District Descriptions,* identify the 1910 enumeration district number assigned within States, counties, and cities. The descriptions are arranged alphabetically by State.

A list of rolls 28-40 of T1224 follows. Appendix III of this catalog lists the enumeration districts within cities that had populations of more than 50,000. Prices and ordering procedures for T1224 are the same as for the census schedules and Soundex/Miracode.

Microfilm Publication T1224

Census Enumeration District Descriptions (1910)

Roll 28—Alabama, Arizona, Arkansas, California, Colorado, Connecticut, Delaware, District of Columbia, and Florida

CENSUS MICROFILM RENTAL PROGRAM
P.O. Box 30
Annapolis Junction, MD 20701-0030

FROM			
LIBRARY			
STREET ADDRESS			
CITY, STATE, ZIP			
ACCOUNT NO.	LIBRARY CONTACT PERSON		TELEPHONE NO.

- Payments accompanying orders should be made payable to Census Microfilm Rental Program

- Deposit Account Customers receive a $.05/per reel discount

- Please enter your orders carefully in the space provided below. Be sure that you have used the correct microfilm publication number and roll number as provided in the National Archives & Record Service Catalog.

PUBLICATION NO.	ROLL NO.	DATE WANTED IF OTHER THAN ASAP	LIBRARY COMMENTS

TOTAL ROLLS ORDERED	TOTAL ORDER AMOUNT	DATE ORDER MAILED	

THIS ORDER FORM MAY BE PHOTOCOPIED

CENSUS MICROFILM RENTAL PROGRAM
P.O. Box 30
Annapolis Junction, MD 20701-0030

LIBRARY		
STREET ADDRESS		
CITY, STATE, ZIP		

F R O M

ACCOUNT NO.	LIBRARY CONTACT PERSON	TELEPHONE NO.

- Payments accompanying orders should be made payable to Census Microfilm Rental Program

- Deposit Account Customers receive a $.05/per reel discount

- Please enter your orders carefully in the space provided below. Be sure that you have used the correct microfilm publication number and roll number as provided in the National Archives & Record Service Catalog.

PUBLICATION NO.	ROLL NO.	DATE WANTED IF OTHER THAN ASAP	LIBRARY COMMENTS

TOTAL ROLLS ORDERED	TOTAL ORDER AMOUNT	DATE ORDER MAILED	

THIS ORDER FORM MAY BE PHOTOCOPIED

1910 Census Schedules
T624. 1,784 rolls.

The 1910 census schedules are arranged by State or Territory and thereunder by county. In some instances the names of large cities also appear. The entries may not be in strict alphabetical order. Be sure to review the listings for the entire State or Territory before placing your order.

Entries also include enumeration district numbers. If you wish to order the census schedules for a minor civil division or geographic area within a particular county or a certain ward within a given city, it is necessary for you to know the enumeration district number assigned to that place. Sometimes the schedule for a county or a city has been filmed on more than one roll, and the correct enumeration district number is needed in order to select the correct roll. Descriptions of census enumeration districts for the 1910 census are reproduced on rolls 28-40 of microfilm publication T1224 (see page vi of this catalog).

ALABAMA

1. Autauga, Baldwin, and Barbour (ED's 1–12) Counties.
2. Barbour (ED's 13–26), Bibb, and Blount Counties.
3. Bullock and Butler (ED's 16–25, 29) Counties.
4. Butler (ED's 26–28, 30–33) and Calhoun Counties.
5. Chambers and Cherokee Counties.
6. Chilton, Choctaw, and Clarke Counties.
7. Clay, Cleburne, and Coffee Counties.
8. Colbert, Conecuh, and Coosa Counties.
9. Covington and Crenshaw Counties.
10. Cullman, De Kalb (ED's 35–43, *see also* roll 12), and Dale Counties.
11. Dallas County.
12. De Kalb (ED's 44–55, *see also* roll 10), Elmore, and Geneva (ED's 95–99, *see also* roll 14) Counties.
13. Escambia, Etowah, and Fayette Counties.
14. Franklin, Geneva (ED's 100–114, *see also* roll 12), and Greene (ED's 19–35) Counties.
15. Greene (ED's 36–48, 194), Hale, Limestone (ED's 94–98, see also roll 22), and Henry Counties.
16. Houston and Jackson Counties.
17. Jefferson (ED's 30–41, 93, 105–128) County.
18. Jefferson (ED's 42–60, 129–136) County.
19. Jefferson (ED's 61–87, 154) County.
20. Jefferson (ED's 88–92, 94–104), Lamar, and Lauderdale (ED's 49–57, 71–73) Counties.
21. Lauderdale (ED's 58–70), Lawrence, and Lee (ED's 157–168) Counties.
22. Lee (ED's 169–173, 175–180), Limestone (ED's 99–110, 173, *see also* roll 15), and Lowndes Counties.
23. Macon and Madison (ED's 111–129) Counties.
24. Madison (ED's 130–145) and Marengo Counties.
25. Marion, Marshall, and Monroe Counties.
26. Mobile (ED's 61–77) County.
27. Mobile (ED's 78–117) County.
28. Montgomery (ED's 83–90, 102–124) County.
29. Montgomery (ED's 91–101) and Morgan Counties.
30. Perry and Pickens Counties.
31. Pike and Randolph Counties.
32. Russell, St. Clair, and Shelby (ED's 102–113) Counties.
33. Shelby (ED's 114–119), Sumter, and Talladega (ED's 120–130, 143) Counties.
34. Talladega (ED's 131–142) and Tallapoosa Counties.
35. Tuscaloosa and Walker (ED's 170–180, 192, 193, 196, 197) Counties.
36. Walker (ED's 181–191, 195), Washington, and Wilcox (ED's 144–154) Counties.
37. Wilcox (ED's 155–168) and Winston Counties.

ARIZONA

38. Apache and Cochise Counties.
39. Coconino, Gila, and Graham Counties.
40. Maricopa County.
41. Mohave, Yuma, Navajo, and Pima Counties.
42. Pinal, Santa Cruz, and Yavapai Counties.

ARKANSAS

43. Arkansas, Ashley, Baxter, and Boone Counties.
44. Benton, Bradley, and Calhoun Counties.
45. Carroll, Chicot, and Clark Counties.
46. Clay, Cleburne, Cleveland, and Columbia Counties.
47. Conway and Craighead Counties.
48. Crawford, Crittenden, Cross, and Dallas Counties.
49. Desha, Drew, and Faulkner Counties.
50. Franklin, Fulton, and Garland Counties.
51. Grant, Hot Springs, and Greene Counties.
52. Hempstead, Howard, and Independence Counties.
53. Izard, Lafayette, and Jackson Counties.
54. Jefferson and Johnson Counties.
55. Lawrence, Lee, Little River, and Lincoln Counties.
56. Logan and Lonoke Counties.
57. Madison, Marion, and Miller Counties.
58. Mississippi and Monroe Counties.
59. Newton, Montgomery, Nevada, and Ouachita Counties.
60. Perry, Phillips, and Pike Counties.
61. Poinsett, Prairie, Polk, and Pope Counties.
62. Pulaski (ED's 98–144) County.
63. Pulaski (ED's 145–157), Randolph, and St. Francis Counties.
64. Saline, Scott, Sharp, Searcy, and Stone Counties.
65. Sebastian County.
66. Sevier, Union, and Van Buren Counties.
67. Washington and White Counties.
68. Woodruff and Yell Counties.

CALIFORNIA

69. Alameda (ED's 1–17, 30–37, 39, 74–86, 215, 216) County.
70. Alameda (ED's 87–126, 214) County.
71. Alameda (ED's 18–29, 127–150, 207–213) County.
72. Alameda (ED's 38, 40–73, 151–160, 218) County.
73. Alpine, Amador, Calaveras, and Butte (ED's 1–13, 197–201) Counties.
74. Butte (ED's 14–18), Colusa, Del Norte, and El Dorado Counties.
75. Contra Costa and Fresno (ED's 26–28, 42, 45–50, 179) Counties.
76. Fresno (ED's 29–41, 43, 44, 51–73, 176–178, 183) County.
77. Glenn, Imperial, and Humboldt Counties.
78. Inyo, Lake, Lassen, and Kern Counties.
79. Kings and Los Angeles (ED's 1–16, 71, 113–116, 278, 348, 360, 369) Counties.
80. Los Angeles (ED's 117–127, 207, 213–242, 275, 359, 364) County.
81. Los Angeles (ED's 128–133, 138–144, 153, 154, 243–274, 365) County.
82. Los Angeles (ED's 104, 105, 134–137, 145–152, 155–164, 168–173, 176–181, 185, 189, 193–206, 208–212, 361) County.
83. Los Angeles (ED's 46–70, 72, 73, 165–167, 174, 175, 182–184, 186–188, 190–192, 355) County.
84. Los Angeles (ED's 74–103, 106–112, 276, 277, 279, 362, 363) County.
85. Los Angeles (ED's 17–45, 280–291, 320, 349, 354) County.
86. Los Angeles (ED's 292–319, 321–323, 336–339, 341, 350, 356–358, 366, 368) County.
87. Los Angeles (ED's 324–335, 340, 342–347, 351–353, 367), Madera, Mariposa, and Modoc Counties.
88. Marin and Mendocino Counties.
89. Merced, Mono, and Monterey Counties.
90. Napa, Nevada, and Orange Counties.
91. Placer, Plumas, and Riverside Counties.
92. Sacramento (ED's 87–115, 131–135) County.
93. Sacramento (ED's 116–130, 196), San Benito, and San Bernardino (ED's 91, 93–96, 104) Counties.
94. San Bernardino (ED's 92, 97–103, 105–124, 224, 226, 228) and San Diego (ED's 140–152) Counties.
95. San Diego (ED's 125–139, 153–165, 239) and San Francisco (ED's 1–6, 13–19) Counties.
96. San Francisco (ED's 7–12, 20–58, 139–150) County.
97. San Francisco (ED's 59–101) County.
98. San Francisco (ED's 102–166) County.
99. San Francisco (ED's 167–205) County.
100. San Francisco (ED's 206–242) County.
101. San Francisco (ED's 243–294) County.

102. San Francisco (ED's 295-315) and San Joaquin (ED's 113-117, 121-126, 185) Counties.

103. San Joaquin (ED's 118-149, 173) County.

104. San Luis Obispo, San Mateo, and Santa Barbara (ED's 168-174, 221) Counties.

105. Santa Barbara (ED's 166, 167, 175-186, 234) and Santa Clara (ED's 62-90) Counties.

106. Santa Clara (ED's 91-115) and Santa Cruz (ED's 116-132) Counties.

107. Santa Cruz (ED's 133-136), Sierra, Sutter, and Shasta Counties.

108. Siskiyou, Solano, and Tehama Counties.

109. Sonoma County.

110. Stanislaus, Trinity, Yolo, and Tulare (ED's 187-196, 200, 225, 227, 229, 241) Counties.

111. Tulare (ED's 197-199, 201-207, 223, 232), Tuolumne, Yuba, and Ventura Counties.

COLORADO

112. Adams, Arapahoe, Archuleta, Baca, Bent, Chaffee, Cheyenne, and Clear Creek Counties.

113. Boulder, Conejos, Costilla, and Custer Counties.

114. Delta, Dolores, Douglas, Eagle, and Denver (ED's 47-74) Counties.

115. Denver (ED's 75-105, 141-150) County.

116. Denver (ED's 106-140, 151-162) County.

117. Denver (ED's 163-183, 197-206) County.

118. Denver (ED's 184-196) and El Paso (ED's 17-37, 200) Counties.

119. El Paso (ED's 38-59), Elbert, and Fremont Counties.

120. Garfield, Gilpin, Grand, Gunnison, Hinsdale, Huerfano, Jackson, Jefferson, Kiowa, and Kit Carson Counties.

121. La Plata, Lake, Larimer, and Las Animas (ED's 95-105) Counties.

122. Las Animas (ED's 106-120, 199), Lincoln, Logan, Mineral, and Mesa Counties.

123. Montezuma, Montrose, Morgan, Otero, Ouray, Park, and Prowers Counties.

124. Phillips, Pitkin, Yuma, and Pueblo Counties.

125. Rio Blanco, Rio Grande, Routt, Saguache, San Juan, San Miguel, Sedgwick, Summit, Teller, and Washington Counties.

126. Weld County.

CONNECTICUT

127. Fairfield (ED's 1, 2, 58, 73-91, 103-108, 119-126) County.

128. Fairfield (ED's 3-37) County.

129. Fairfield (ED's 38-57, 59-72, 601, 604, 609) County.

130. Fairfield (ED's 92-102, 109-118, 600, 607) and Hartford (ED's 127-137) Counties.

131. Hartford (ED's 138-153, 208-215, 234-237, 247, 248) County.

132. Hartford (ED's 154-174, 238-246, 605) County.

133. Hartford (ED's 175-207, 606, 608) County.

134. Hartford (ED's 216-233) and Litchfield (ED's 249-264) Counties.

135. Litchfield (ED's 265-290) and Middlesex (ED's 291-302, 313-317, 599) Counties.

136. Middlesex (ED's 303-312, 602) and New Haven (ED's 328-343, 362-364, 444, 445) Counties.

137. New Haven (ED's 318-327, 365-371, 446-461, 495, 496, 603) County.

138. New Haven (ED's 344-361, 372-386, 437-443) County.

139. New Haven (ED's 387-413, 428-430) County.

140. New Haven (ED's 414-427, 431-436, 462-476) County.

141. New Haven (ED's 477-494) and New London (ED's 497-507) Counties.

142. New London (ED's 508-530, 542-551) County.

143. New London (ED's 531-541), Tolland, and Windham (ED's 568-576) Counties.

144. Windham (ED's 577-598) County.

DELAWARE

145. Kent County.

146. New Castle (ED's 21-28, 31-35, 71-100) County.

147. New Castle (ED's 29, 30, 36-70) County.

148. Sussex County.

DISTRICT OF COLUMBIA

149. ED's 1-33, 230-238, 240.

150. ED's 34-57, 241, 245.

151. ED's 58-95.

152. ED's 96-139, 242.

153. ED's 140-167, 244.

154. ED's 168-198, 239.

155. ED's 199-229, 243.

FLORIDA

156. Alachua County.

157. Baker, Bradford, Brevard, and Calhoun Counties.

158. Citrus, Clay, Dade, Columbia, De Soto, Franklin, and Duval (ED's 60-67) Counties.

159. Duval (ED's 68-93) County.

160. Escambia and Gadsden Counties.

161. Hamilton, Hernando, and Hillsborough (ED's 19-39, 43) Counties.

162. Hillsborough (ED's 40-42, 44-63, 157) and Holmes Counties.

163. Lafayette, Jackson, Jefferson, Lake, and Lee Counties.

164. Leon, Levy, Manatee, Liberty, and Madison Counties.

165. Marion and Monroe Counties.

166. Nassau, Osceola, Palm Beach, Orange, Pasco, and Putnam Counties.

167. Polk, St. Johns, St. Lucie, Santa Rosa, and Sumter Counties.

168. Suwannee, Taylor, and Volusia Counties.

169. Wakulla, Walton, and Washington Counties.

GEORGIA

170. Appling, Butts, Baker, and Baldwin Counties.

171. Banks, Bryan, Camden, and Bartow Counties.

172. Ben Hill, Chattooga, Berrien, and Bibb (ED's 14-17) Counties.

173. Bibb (ED's 11-13, 18-46) County.

174. Brooks and Bulloch Counties.

175. Burke, Calhoun, Campbell, and Carroll (ED's 1, 2, 5) Counties.

176. Carroll (ED's 3, 4, 6-22), Catoosa, Clayton, and Clinch Counties.

177. Charlton, Dooly, and Chatham (ED's 33-51) Counties.

178. Chatham (ED's 52-87) County.

179. Chattahoochee, Colquitt, Cherokee, and Clay Counties.

180. Clarke and Cobb Counties.

181. Coffee, Dade, Columbia, Crawford, and Dawson Counties.

182. Coweta, Fannin, and Gilmer Counties.

183. Crisp, Douglas, and Decatur (ED's 49-62) Counties.

184. Decatur (ED's 63, 64), Early, Echols, and De Kalb Counties.

185. Dodge, Glascock, Dougherty, and Effingham Counties.

186. Elbert and Emanuel Counties.

187. Fayette, Glynn, and Floyd (ED's 56-75, 163) Counties.

188. Floyd (ED's 76-82), Gordon, Forsyth, and Haralson Counties.

189. Franklin, Grady, and Hart Counties.

190. Fulton (ED's 42-57, 106, 110-119, 172, 174) County.

191. Fulton (ED's 58-78, 171) County.

192. Fulton (ED's 79-104, 170, 173, 175) County.

193. Fulton (ED's 120-135), Greene, and Heard (ED's 59-63) Counties.

194. Heard (ED's 64-66), Jefferson, and Gwinnett (ED's 53-67) Counties.

195. Gwinnett (ED's 68, 69), Houston, Habersham, Irwin, and Jackson (ED's 94-96) Counties.

196. Jackson (ED's 97-111) and Hall Counties.

197. Hancock, Harris, and Macon Counties.
198. Henry, Jeff Davis, Jasper, and Laurens (ED's 100–104) Counties.
199. Laurens (ED's 97–99, 105–116), Jenkins, Lincoln, and Lumpkin Counties.
200. Johnson, Jones, Lee, and Monroe (ED's 88–98) Counties.
201. Monroe (ED's 99–103), Montgomery, Liberty, Miller, and Quitman Counties.
202. Lowndes, McDuffie, McIntosh, and Marion Counties.
203. Madison, Pickens, and Meriwether Counties.
204. Milton, Newton, Mitchell, and Morgan (ED's 100–102) Counties.
205. Morgan (ED's 103–115), Murray, and Muscogee (ED's 93–114) Counties.
206. Muscogee (ED's 92, 115–119), Oconee, Towns, Oglethorpe, and Paulding (ED's 114–119) Counties.
207. Paulding (ED's 120–124), Pierce, Rockdale, Pike, and Polk (ED's 129–132) Counties.
208. Polk (ED's 125–128, 133–138), Putnam, Pulaski, and Spalding (ED's 125, 126) Counties.
209. Spalding (ED's 116–124), Taylor, Rabun, Stewart, and Union Counties.
210. Randolph and Richmond (ED's 49–61, 74, 79–81, 83) Counties.
211. Richmond (ED's 62–73, 75–78, 82), Schley, and Screven Counties.
212. Stephens, Taliaferro, Tattnall, and Telfair Counties.
213. Sumter and Wilkes Counties.
214. Talbot, Walker, and Ware Counties.
215. Terrell and Thomas Counties.
216. Tift, Toombs, and Washington Counties.
217. Troup, Turner, Twiggs, and White Counties.
218. Upson, Wayne, and Walton Counties.
219. Warren, Wilcox, Webster, and Worth Counties.
220. Whitfield and Wilkinson Counties.

IDAHO

221. Ada and Bannock Counties.
222. Bear Lake, Blaine, Boise, Bingham, and Blackfoot Counties.
223. Bonner, Cassia, and Canyon Counties.
224. Custer, Elmore, Idaho, and Fremont Counties.
225. Kootenai and Latah Counties.
226. Lemhi, Lincoln, and Nez Perce Counties.
227. Oneida, Owyhee, and Shoshone Counties.
228. Twin Falls and Washington Counties.

ILLINOIS

229. Adams (ED's 1–37, 43–54, 61, 202) County.
230. Adams (ED's 38–42, 55–60), Bond, and Alexander Counties.
231. Boone, Brown, and Bureau (ED's 1–21) Counties.
232. Bureau (ED's 22–33), Calhoun, Carroll, and Cass (ED's 16–19, 27–29) Counties.
233. Cass (ED's 20–26), Clay, and Champaign (ED's 1–20, 22–24) Counties.
234. Champaign (ED's 21, 25–42) and Christian (ED's 1–25) Counties.
235. Christian (ED's 26–32), Ford, and Clark Counties.
236. Clinton and Coles (ED's 43–63) Counties.
237. Coles (ED's 64–69), De Witt, and Cook (ED's 1–16, 1650) Counties.
238. Cook (ED's 17–27, 29, 33–46, 58–65, 1534–1539, 1543, 1648, 1655–1657) County.
239. Cook (ED's 28, 47–57, 66–85, 135–139, 1565, 1582) County.
240. Cook (ED's 30–32, 86–113, 1540–1542, 1649) County.
241. Cook (ED's 114–134, 140–167, 1544, 1601, 1632) County.
242. Cook (ED's 168–220, 1581, 1643) County.
243. Cook (ED's 221–260, 1580, 1613) County.
244. Cook (ED's 261–292) County.
245. Cook (ED's 293–332) County.

246. Cook (ED's 333–376) County.
247. Cook (ED's 377–418, 1550, 1586) County.
248. Cook (ED's 419–459, 1560) County. @03249.
249. Cook (ED's 460–478, 480–490, 492–502, 1549, 1571, 1597, 1606, 1615, 1641, 1642) County.
250. Cook (ED's 505–524, 1589, 1605, 1609, 1618, 1624, 1630) County.
251. Cook (ED's 525–545, 1557, 1607, 1608, 1631, 1633, 1634) County.
252. Cook (ED's 546–570) County.
253. Cook (ED's 571–603) County.
254. Cook (ED's 604–615, 618–635) County.
255. Cook (ED's 636–673, 1553, 1594, 1638, 1639) County.
256. Cook (ED's 674–710, 1552, 1562, 1573, 1575, 1576) County.
257. Cook (ED's 711–739, 1610, 1621, 1622, 1640) County.
258. Cook (ED's 740–764, 1627) County.
259. Cook (ED's 765–784, 1568, 1596, 1602) County.
260. Cook (ED's 785–803, 830–833, 1558, 1559, 1566, 1567, 1652) County.
261. Cook (ED's 834–854, 1579, 1590, 1620, 1647) County.
262. Cook (ED's 804–829, 855–876, 1554–1556, 1574, 1595) County.
263. Cook (ED's 877–913, 1653) County.
264. Cook (ED's 914–955) County.
265. Cook (ED's 956–969, 1001–1016, 1577, 1611) County.
266. Cook (ED's 970–988, 1017–1032, 1625) County.
267. Cook (ED's 989–1000, 1033–1047, 1049–1055, 1587, 1619, 1646) County.
268. Cook (ED's 1056–1060, 1062–1088, 1090–1093) County.
269. Cook (ED's 1094–1102, 1155–1176, 1564, 1626) County.
270. Cook (ED's 1178–1206, 1612, 1616) County.
271. Cook (ED's 1103–1123, 1207–1217, 1578, 1617, 1628, 1629, 1651) County.
272. Cook (ED's 1124–1154, 1591, 1614) County.
273. Cook (ED's 1218–1247, 1593, 1636) County.
274. Cook (ED's 1248–1270, 1545, 1546, 1588, 1600, 1604, 1623, 1635) County.
275. Cook (ED's 1271–1293, 1547, 1548, 1569, 1570, 1583, 1603) County.
276. Cook (ED's 1294–1327, 1572, 1598) County.
277. Cook (ED's 1328–1358, 1584, 1645) County.
278. Cook (ED's 1359–1392, 1563, 1585, 1592, 1599) County.
279. Cook (ED's 1393–1427, 1551, 1644) County.
280. Cook (ED's 1428–1453, 1637) County.
281. Cook (ED's 1454–1486) County.
282. Cook (ED's 1487–1517, 1561) County.
283. Cook (ED's 1518–1533) and Crawford Counties.
284. Cumberland, Edwards, and De Kalb (ED's 14–35) Counties.
285. De Kalb (ED's 36–41), Douglas, and Du Page (ED's 1–9, 11, 14, 15, 206) Counties.
286. Du Page (ED's 10, 12, 13), Effingham, and Edgar Counties.
287. Fayette and Franklin Counties.
288. Fulton County.
289. Gallatin, Henderson, Greene, and Hancock (ED's 1, 5, 6) Counties.
290. Hancock (ED's 2–4, 7–29) and Grundy Counties.
291. Hamilton, Hardin, and Henry (ED's 105–122, 138–142, 201, 203) Counties.
292. Henry (ED's 123–137) and Iroquois Counties.
293. Jackson and Jasper Counties.
294. Jefferson and Jo Daviess Counties.
295. Jersey, Kendall, Johnson, and Kane (ED's 16, 17, 44–50) Counties.
296. Kane (ED's 18–43, 51–57, 79–89) County.
297. Kane (ED's 58–78, 90, 91) and Lawrence Counties.
298. Kankakee and Knox (ED's 143–147, 169–173) Counties.

299. Knox (ED's 148–168, 174–184) and La Salle (ED's 76–85, 95) Counties.

300. La Salle (ED's 73–75, 86–94, 96–118) County.

301. La Salle (ED's 119–139) and Lake (ED's 92–104, 108, 205) Counties.

302. Lake (ED's 105–107, 109–120) and Lee Counties.

303. Livingston and Logan (ED's 51–54, 56–62) Counties.

304. Logan (ED's 55, 63–73) and McHenry Counties.

305. McDonough and McLean (ED's 74–77, 95–111) Counties.

306. McLean (ED's 78–94, 112–123) and Marion (ED's 131, 132, 140–145) Counties.

307. Marion (ED's 133–139, 146–156) and Macon (ED's 106–115, 119, 120) Counties.

308. Macon (ED's 101–105, 116–118, 121–135) and Macoupin (ED's 33–55, 60) Counties.

309. Macoupin (ED's 56–59, 61–78) and Madison (ED's 14–30, 40–42) Counties.

310. Madison (ED's 31–39, 43–69) County.

311. Marshall, Mason, and Mercer Counties.

312. Massac, Menard, Monroe, and Montgomery (ED's 79–89) Counties.

313. Montgomery (ED's 90–110) and Morgan (ED's 90–111) Counties.

314. Morgan (ED's 112–119), Moultrie, and Ogle (ED's 64–84, 153) Counties.

315. Ogle (ED's 85–87), Perry, and Peoria (ED's 49–55, 67–70, 91–95) Counties.

316. Peoria (ED's 71–90, 96–107, 158) County.

317. Peoria (ED's 56–66, 108–115), Piatt, and Scott Counties.

318. Pike, Putnam, and Richland Counties.

319. Pope, Pulaski, and Randolph (ED's 95–114, 116–118) Counties.

320. Randolph (ED's 115, 119–121) and Rock Island (ED's 82–111, 128–132, 153) Counties.

321. Rock Island (ED's 112–127, 155) and St. Clair (ED's 82–101) Counties.

322. St. Clair (ED's 102–130, 136–140) County.

323. St. Clair (ED's 131–135, 141–163) and Stark Counties.

324. Saline and Sangamon (ED's 111–115, 158–171) Counties.

325. Sangamon (ED's 116–157) County.

326. Sangamon (ED's 172–184) and Shelby Counties.

327. Schuyler and Stephenson Counties.

328. Tazewell and Washington Counties.

329. Union and Vermilion (ED's 123–134, 159–165) Counties.

330. Vermilion (ED's 135–158, 166–187) County.

331. Wabash and Whiteside Counties.

332. Warren and Wayne Counties.

333. White and Will (ED's 142–152, 183–197) Counties.

334. Will (ED's 153–182) County.

335. Will (ED's 198–204) and Williamson Counties.

336. Winnebago (ED's 140–147, 150–175, 181) County.

337. Winnebago (ED's 148, 149, 176–180) and Woodford Counties.

INDIANA

338. Adams and Allen (ED's 1–27, 29, 30) Counties.

339. Allen (ED's 28, 31–69) County.

340. Bartholomew, Benton, Brown, and Blackford Counties.

341. Boone, Carroll, and Cass (ED's 16–20, 33–44) Counties.

342. Cass (ED's 21–32) and Clark Counties.

343. Clay and Clinton Counties.

344. Crawford, Newton, and Daviess Counties. 208345.

Dearborn, Decatur, and De Kalb Counties.

346. Delaware County.

347. Dubois and Elkhart (ED's 1–21) Counties.

348. Elkhart (ED's 22–49), Fayette, and Floyd (ED's 60–68) Counties.

349. Floyd (ED's 69–84) and Fountain Counties.

350. Franklin, Fulton, and Gibson (ED's 1–11, 24, 25) Counties.

351. Gibson (ED's 12–23) and Grant (ED's 45–47, 60–81) Counties.

352. Grant (ED's 48–59) and Greene Counties.

353. Hamilton and Hancock Counties.

354. Harrison and Hendricks Counties.

355. Henry and Howard (ED's 118, 119, 137–150) Counties.

356. Howard (ED's 120–136) and Huntington Counties.

357. Jackson, Jasper, and Kosciusko (ED's 88–95) Counties.

358. Kosciusko (ED's 66–87) and Jay Counties.

359. Jefferson, Jennings, and Johnson Counties.

360. Knox County.

361. Lagrange and Lake (ED's 50–71) Counties.

362. Lake (ED's 31–49, 72–79) County.

363. La Porte County.

364. Lawrence and Madison (ED's 84–86, 100–114) Counties.

365. Madison (ED's 87–99, 115–128) and Marion (ED's 1–11, 18–20, 268) County.

366. Marion (ED's 12–17, 21–61) County.

367. Marion (ED's 62–122, 239–250, 269) County.

368. Marion (ED's 123–191) County.

369. Marion (ED's 192–238, 251–267) County.

370. Marshall, Martin, and Miami (ED's 111–119) Counties.

371. Miami (ED's 120–140), Monroe, and Montgomery (ED's 151–164, 176–179) Counties.

372. Montgomery (ED's 165–175, 198), Ohio, Morgan, and Noble Counties.

373. Orange, Owen, and Parke Counties.

374. Perry, Pike, and Porter Counties.

375. Posey, Pulaski, Warren, and Putnam Counties.

376. Randolph and Ripley Counties.

377. Rush and St. Joseph (ED's 132–157, 194–196, 208) Counties.

378. St. Joseph (ED's 158–193) County.

379. Scott, Starke, and Shelby Counties.

380. Spencer, Steuben, and Sullivan (ED's 161–169) Counties.

381. Sullivan (ED's 170–178, 180), Switzerland, Union, and Tippecanoe (ED's 154, 174–193) Counties.

382. Tippecanoe (ED's 155–173), Tipton, and Vanderburgh (ED's 85–87, 147–158) Counties.

383. Vanderburgh (ED's 88–146) County.

384. Vermillion and Vigo (ED's 129–133, 174–196) Counties.

385. Vigo (ED's 134–173, 198, 199) County.

386. Wabash and Warrick Counties.

387. Washington and Wayne (ED's 162–186, 203) Counties.

388. Wayne (ED's 187–202) and Wells Counties.

389. White and Whitley Counties.

IOWA

390. Adair, Adams, Allamakee, and Appanoose (ED's 12–21, 28, 29) Counties.

391. Appanoose (ED's 22–27, 30, 31), Audubon, and Benton Counties.

392. Black Hawk and Boone (ED's 1–15, 23, 236) Counties.

393. Boone (ED's 16–22), Hancock, Bremer, and Buchanan Counties.

394. Buena Vista, Butler, and Calhoun Counties.

395. Carroll, Cass, and Cedar Counties.

396. Cerro Gordo, Cherokee, Chickasaw, and Dickinson Counties.

397. Clarke, Clay, and Clayton Counties.

398. Clinton County.

399. Crawford, Dallas, Davis, and Emmet Counties.

400. Decatur, Delaware, and Des Moines (ED's 1, 2, 14–27) Counties.

401. Des Moines (ED's 3–13) and Dubuque (ED's 106–125, 138–148) Counties.

402. Dubuque (ED's 126–137), Fayette, and Floyd Counties.

403. Franklin, Fremont, Grundy, and Greene Counties.

404. Guthrie, Hamilton, and Hardin Counties.

405. Harrison and Henry Counties.

406. Howard, Humboldt, Ida, and Lyon Counties.

407. Iowa, Jackson, and Jasper (ED's 17–36) Counties.

408. Jasper (ED's 37–41), Jefferson, and Johnson Counties.

409. Jones, Keokuk, and Kossuth Counties.

410. Lee and Linn (ED's 75–90, 95–97, 121, 122) Counties.

411. Linn (ED's 91–94, 98–120, 171, 172, 176), Louisa, and and Lucas Counties.

412. Madison, Mahaska, and Marion (ED's 40–54) Counties.

413. Marion (ED's 55–61), Marshall, Mills, and Mitchell (ED's 130–134, 137, 138) Counties.

414. Mitchell (ED's 135, 136, 139–143), Monona, and Monroe Counties.

415. Montgomery and Muscatine Counties.

416. O'Brien, Osceola, and Pocahontas Counties.

417. Page, Palo Alto, and Ringgold Counties.

418. Plymouth and Polk (ED's 62–68, 172–184) Counties.

419. Polk (ED's 69–119) County.

420. Polk (ED's 120–171) and Pottawattamie (ED's 119–128, 147–154, 180) Counties.

421. Pottawattamie (ED's 129–146, 155–162) and Poweshiek Counties.

422. Sac and Scott (ED's 122–137, 151–161) Counties.

423. Scott (ED's 138–150), Shelby, and Sioux Counties.

424. Story and Tama Counties.

425. Taylor, Union, Van Buren, and Winnebago (ED's 225–229, see also roll 427) Counties.

426. Wapello and Warren Counties.

427. Washington, Wayne, and Winnebago (ED's 230–235, see also roll 425) Counties.

428. Webster and Winneshiek (ED's 144–160) Counties.

429. Winneshiek (ED's 161–166), Worth, and Woodbury (ED's 161–192, 215–219) Counties.

430. Woodbury (ED's 193–214, 221) and Wright Counties.

KANSAS

431. Allen, Anderson, and Atchison (ED's 1–13) Counties.

432. Atchison (ED's 14–19), Barber, Barton, and Bourbon Counties.

433. Brown, Butler, Chase, and Chautauqua Counties.

434. Cherokee, Cheyenne, Clark, and Clay Counties.

435. Cloud, Coffey, Comanche, and Cowley (ED's 45–53, 55–57) Counties.

436. Cowley (ED's 54, 58–72) and Crawford (ED's 73–105) Counties.

437. Crawford (ED's 106–117), Decatur, Doniphan, and Dickinson Counties.

438. Douglas, Edwards, and Ellis Counties.

439. Elk, Ellsworth, Finney, Ford, and Franklin Counties.

440. Geary, Gove, Graham, Grant, Gray, Greeley, Haskell, and Hodgeman Counties.

441. Greenwood, Hamilton, Harper, Kearny, and Harvey Counties.

442. Jackson, Lane, Jefferson, Meade, and Jewell Counties.

443. Johnson, Kingman, Kiowa, and Labette (ED's 138–153) Counties.

444. Labette (ED's 127–137), Lincoln, and Leavenworth Counties.

445. Linn, Logan, and Lyon Counties.

446. McPherson and Marion Counties.

447. Marshall and Miami Counties.

448. Mitchell, Ness, and Montgomery (ED's 154–186) Counties.

449. Montgomery (ED's 187–192), Morton (ED's 105–118, 233, see also roll 450), Morris, and Woodson Counties.

450. Morton (ED 111, see also roll 449), Pottawatomie, Scott, and Nemaha Counties.

451. Neosho, Osage, and Seward Counties.

452. Osborne, Rooks, Ottawa, Pawnee, Phillips, and Rush Counties.

453. Pratt, Rawlins, and Reno Counties.

454. Republic, Rice, Sheridan, Riley, and Sherman Counties.

455. Russell, Stanton, Stevens, Wallace, Wichita, Saline, and Sedgwick (ED's 78, 79, 81–99) Counties.

456. Sedgwick (ED's 80, 100–146) County.

457. Shawnee County.

458. Smith, Thomas, Stafford, Trego, and Sumner (ED's 148–170, 176) Counties.

459. Sumner (ED's 147, 171–175), Wabaunsee, Washington, and Wilson Counties.

460. Wyandotte (ED's 144–168, 192–207) County.

461. Wyandotte (ED's 169–191, 208) County.

KENTUCKY

462. Adair, Boone, Allen, and Anderson Counties.

463. Ballard, Bath, and Barren Counties.

464. Bell and Boyd Counties.

465. Bourbon, Carroll, Boyle, and Bracken Counties.

466. Breathitt and Campbell (ED's 10–27, 31–35, 48–51) Counties.

467. Campbell (ED's 28–30, 36–47, 52–58), Breckinridge, and Caldwell (ED's 13–16) Counties.

468. Caldwell (ED's 10–12, 17, 18), Clark, Bullitt, and Butler Counties.

469. Calloway, Carter and Edmonson Counties.

470. Carlisle, Casey, and Christian (ED's 1–18) Counties.

471. Christian (ED's 19–27), Garrard, Clay, and Clinton Counties.

472. Crittenden, Estill, Cumberland, and Daviess (ED's 28–36, 142) Counties.

473. Daviess (ED's 37–54), Elliott, and Fleming Counties.

474. Fayette and Gallatin Counties. 208475.

Floyd and Graves Counties.

476. Franklin, Grant, and Greenup Counties.

477. Fulton, Harlan, Grayson, and Hardin (ED's 48–51) Counties.

478. Hardin (ED's 52–62), Lee, Green, and Henry Counties.

479. Hancock, Harrison, Hart, and Henderson (ED's 62–66) Counties.

480. Henderson (ED's 67–83), Hickman, and Johnson Counties.

481. Hopkins and Marion Counties.

482. Jackson, Jessamine, Knott, and Lewis Counties.

483. Jefferson (ED's 1–43) County.

484. Jefferson (ED's 44–85) County.

485. Jefferson (ED's 86–135, 227) County.

486. Jefferson (ED's 136–187, 228) County.

487. Jefferson (ED's 188–226) County.

488. Kenton (ED's 80–124) County.

489. Kenton (ED's 125–135), Leslie, Knox, and Larue (ED's 77, 78) Counties.

490. Larue (ED's 79–84), Lincoln, Laurel, and Lawrence (ED's 93–96) Counties. 208491.

Lawrence (ED's 97–108), Letcher, Livingston, and Marshall Counties.

492. Logan, Lyon, and Morgan Countries.

493. McCracken, Meade, and Menifee Counties.

494. McLean, Magoffin, and Madison Counties.

495. Martin, Mason, Mercer, and Metcalfe Counties.

496. Monroe, Montgomery, and Muhlenberg (ED's 73–80, 83–89) Counties.

497. Muhlenberg (ED's 81, 82), Nelson, Robertson, Nicholas, and Owen Counties.

498. Ohio, Oldham, Owsley, and Rowan Counties.

499. Pendleton, Pike, and Spencer Counties.

500. Perry, Rockcastle, Powell, and Pulaski (ED's 182–191, 198–203) Counties.

501. Pulaski (ED's 192–197, 204–213), Trimble, Russell, and Trigg Counties.

502. Scott, Shelby, and Wayne Counties.

503. Simpson, Washington, Taylor, and Woodford Counties.

504. Todd, Wolfe, Union, and Warren (ED's 111, 112, 115, 116) Counties.

505. Warren (ED's 113, 114, 117–129), Webster, and Whitley (238–240, 243) Counties.

506. Whitley (ED's 241, 242, 244–260) County.

LOUISIANA

507. Acadia and Ascension Parishes.
508. Assumption and Avoyelles Parishes.
509. Bienville, Bossier, and Caddo (ED's 27–29, 53–61) Parishes.
510. Caddo (ED's 30–52) and Calcasieu (ED's 28–32, 50–53) Parishes.
511. Calcasieu (ED's 33–49), Caldwell, and Catahoula Parishes.
512. Cameron, Concordia, Claiborne, and De Soto (ED's 62–72) Parishes.
513. De Soto (ED's 73–77), East Carroll, and East Baton Rouge Parishes.
514. East Feliciana, Franklin, and Iberia Parishes.
515. Grant and Iberville Parishes.
516. Jackson, La Salle, Jefferson, and Lafayette (ED's 65–72) Parishes.
517. Lafayette (ED's 73–76), Lafourche, and Lincoln Parishes.
518. Livingston, Madison, Morehouse, and Natchitoches (ED's 78–85) Parishes.
519. Natchitoches (ED's 86–94) and Orleans (ED's 1–26) Parishes.
520. Orleans (ED's 27–70) Parish.
521. Orleans (ED's 71–118) Parish.
522. Orleans (ED's 119–154) Parish.
523. Orleans (ED's 155–190) Parish.
524. Orleans (ED's 191–227, 248) Parish.
525. Orleans (ED's 228–247) and Ouachita Parishes.
526. Plaquemines, Red River, and Pointe Coupee Parishes.
527. Rapides, Richland, and St. Bernard Parishes.
528. Sabine, St. Charles, St. Helena, and St. James Parishes.
529. St. John the Baptist, Terrebonne, and St. Landry (ED's 100–107, 153) Parishes.
530. St. Landry (ED's 108–123, 152) and St. Martin Parishes.
531. St. Mary and St. Tammany Parishes.
532. Tangipahoa, West Baton Rouge, and Tensas Parishes.
533. Union, Vermilion, and Vernon Parishes.
534. Washington and Webster Parishes.
535. West Carroll, West Feliciana, and Winn Parishes.

MAINE

536. Androscoggin County.
537. Aroostook (ED's 1–36) County.
538. Aroostook (ED's 37–48) and Cumberland (ED's 40–60, 101, 109, 116, 117) Counties.
539. Cumberland (ED's 61–100) County.
540. Cumberland (ED's 102–108, 110–115, 118, 119), Franklin, and Hancock (ED's 49–65) Counties.
541. Hancock (ED's 66–82) and Kennebec (ED's 83–117) Counties.
542. Kennebec (ED's 118–133) and Knox Counties.
543. Lincoln and Oxford Counties.
544. Penobscot (ED's 134–181) County.
545. Penobscot (ED's 182–195), Piscataquis, and Sagadahoc Counties.
546. Somerset and Waldo Counties.
547. Washington and York (ED's 222–239) Counties.
548. York (ED's 240–274) County.

MARYLAND

549. Allegany County.
550. Anne Arundel and Baltimore (ED's 1–6, 15–19) Counties.
551. Baltimore (ED's 7–14, 20–40, 57–62, 113, 114) County.
552. Baltimore (41–56, 63–68) County and Baltimore (city) (ED's 1–14).
553. Baltimore (city) (ED's 15–48, 406).
554. Baltimore (city) (ED's 49–92).
555. Baltimore (city) (ED's 93–139).
556. Baltimore (city) (ED's 140–196).
557. Baltimore (city) (ED's 197–249).
558. Baltimore (city) (ED's 250–295).
559. Baltimore (city) (ED's 296–329).
560. Baltimore (city) (ED's 330–363).
561. Baltimore (city) ED's 364–405).
562. Calvert, Howard, Caroline, and Carroll (ED's 69–82) Counties.
563. Carroll (ED's 83–93), Cecil, and Charles Counties.
564. Dorchester and Frederick (ED's 46–70) Counties.
565. Frederick (ED's 71–85), Garrett, and Harford Counties.
566. Kent and Montgomery Counties.
567. Prince Georges and Queen Annes Counties.
568. St. Marys, Somerset, and Talbot Counties.
569. Washington County.
570. Wicomico and Worcester Counties.

MASSACHUSETTS

571. Barnstable and Berkshire (ED's 21–33, 37, 38, 1952) Counties.
572. Berkshire (ED's 34–36, 39–65, 83–87) County.
573. Berkshire (ED's 66–82, 88–95) and Dukes Counties.
574. Bristol (ED's 96–112, 179–181, 220, 221, 1951, 1955) County.
575. Bristol (ED's 113–123, 215–219, 222–227, 248, 249) County.
576. Bristol (ED's 124–151) County.
577. Bristol (ED's 152–178, 1923) County.
578. Bristol (ED's 182–196) County.
579. Bristol (ED's 197–214) County.
580. Bristol (ED's 228–247) and Essex (ED's 257–265, 276) Counties.
581. Essex (ED's 266–275, 277–303, 331, 332) County.
582. Essex (ED's 304–330, 333–338, 340) County.
583. Essex (ED's 339, 341–364, 1937, 1942) County.
584. Essex (ED's 365–380, 389–398, 1950) County.
585. Essex (ED's 381–388, 399–414, 1933) County.
586. Essex (ED's 415–441) County.
587. Essex (ED's 442–463, 475–478) County.
588. Essex (ED's 464–474, 479–487) and Franklin (ED's 488–501) Counties.
589. Franklin (ED's 502–522, 1944) and Hampden (ED's 523–546, 578–582, 1924) Counties.
590. Hampden (ED's 547–577) County.
591. Hampden (ED's 583–602, 610–613, 662–674) County.
592. Hampden (ED's 603–609, 614–630, 651–661, 1936) County.
593. Hampden (ED's 631–650) and Hampshire (ED's 675–690, 694–710) Counties.
594. Hampshire (ED's 691–693, 711–725) and Middlesex (ED's 726–734, 738, 739) Counties.
595. Middlesex (ED's 735–737, 740–746, 755–758, 791–800, 1928) County.
596. Middlesex (ED's 747–754, 759–764, 770–785, 1932, 1940) County.
597. Middlesex (ED's 765–769, 786–790, 801–811, 1939) County.
598. Middlesex (ED's 812–831) County.
599. Middlesex (ED's 832–855, 1954) County.
600. Middlesex (ED's 856–871) County.
601. Middlesex (ED's 872–908) County.
602. Middlesex (ED's 909–955) County.
603. Middlesex (ED's 956–979) County.
604. Middlesex (ED's 987–1003, 1015–1021) County.
605. Middlesex (ED's 980–986, 1004–1014, 1022–1024) County.
606. Middlesex (ED's 1025–1054, 1063–1066) County.
607. Middlesex (ED's 1055–1062, 1067–1077, 1935), Nantucket, and Norfolk (1080–1084, 1097–1100) Counties.
608. Norfolk (ED's 1085–1096, 1101–1118, 1938, 1943) County.
609. Norfolk (ED's 1119–1151) County.
610. Norfolk (ED's 1152–1170) and Plymouth (ED's 1171–1177, 1209–1213, 1930) Counties.
611. Plymouth (ED's 1178–1208) County.
612. Plymouth (ED's 1214–1239) County.

613. Plymouth (ED's 1240–1253) and Suffolk (ED's 1254–1264) Counties.

614. Suffolk (ED's 1265–1302) County.

615. Suffolk (ED's 1303–1340) County.

616. Suffolk (ED's 1341–1381, 1925, 1941, 1945, 1956) County.

617. Suffolk (ED's 1382–1412, 1926, 1948) County.

618. Suffolk (ED's 1413–1442, 1947) County.

619. Suffolk (ED's 1443–1491) County.

620. Suffolk (ED's 1492–1524) County.

621. Suffolk (ED's 1525–1552) County.

622. Suffolk (ED's 1553–1577, 1934) County.

623. Suffolk (ED's 1578–1607) County.

624. Suffolk (ED's 1608–1631) County.

625. Suffolk (ED's 1632–1657, 1929) County.

626. Suffolk (ED's 1658–1691, 1949) County.

627. Worcester (ED's 1692–1723, 1748–1754, 1931) County.

628. Worcester (ED's 1724–1747, 1755–1768) County.

629. Worcester (ED's 1769–1808) County.

630. Worcester (ED's 1809–1849, 1927, 1953) County.

631. Worcester (ED's 1850–1872) County.

632. Worcester (ED's 1873–1893, 1946) County.

633. Worcester (ED's 1894–1922) County.

MICHIGAN

634. Alcona, Alger, and Allegan Counties.

635. Alpena, Baraga, Antrim, and Arenac Counties.

636. Barry, Crawford, and Bay (ED's 33, 37, 38, 53–66) Counties.

637. Bay (ED's 34–36, 39–52) and Benzie Counties.

638. Berrien County.

639. Branch and Calhoun (ED's 25–30, 55–74) Counties.

640. Calhoun (ED's 31–54), Cass, and Charlevoix (ED's 14–19) Counties.

641. Charlevoix (ED's 20–27), Cheboygan, and Chippewa Counties.

642. Clare and Genesee (ED's 1–25, 46–50, 157, 158) Counties.

643. Genesee (ED's 26–45) and Clinton Counties.

644. Delta and Dickinson Counties.

645. Eaton and Emmet Counties.

646. Gladwin and Houghton (ED's 88–93, 100–110, 117–120) Counties.

647. Houghton (ED's 94–99, 111–116, 121–136) and Gogebic Counties.

648. Grand Traverse and Gratiot Counties.

649. Hillsdale and Huron (ED's 1–20) Counties.

650. Huron (ED's 21–29), Ionia, and Iosco Counties.

651. Ingham County.

652. Iron, Kalkaska, and Isabella Counties.

653. Jackson County.

654. Kalamazoo (ED's 122–154, 167) County.

655. Kalamazoo (ED's 155–166, 168) and Kent (ED's 37–49, 124–143, 184) Counties.

656. Kent (ED's 50–71, 118–123, 144–148, 182) County.

657. Kent (ED's 72–88, 95–109, 181) County.

658. Kent (ED's 89–94, 110–117, 183), Keweenaw, Lake, Luce, Mackinac, and Macomb (ED's 57–62) Counties.

659. Macomb (ED's 63–85) and Lapeer Counties. 208660. Leelanau, Livingston, and Lenawee (ED's 43–63) Counties.

661. Lenawee (ED's 64–83) and Manistee Counties.

662. Marquette County.

663. Mason, Oscoda, Mecosta, and Monroe (ED's 84–88) Counties.

664. Monroe (ED's 89–110) and Menominee Counties.

665. Midland, Missaukee, and Montcalm (ED's 142–161) Counties.

666. Montcalm (ED's 162–167), Newaygo, Montmorency, and Wexford Counties.

667. Muskegon and Ontonagon Counties.

668. Oakland County.

669. Oceana, Ogemaw, Osceola, and Otsego Counties.

670. Ottawa and Roscommon Counties.

671. Presque Isle and Saginaw (ED's 24–46, 72–79) County.

672. Saginaw (ED's 47–71, 134) County.

673. St. Clair County.

674. St. Joseph and Sanilac (ED's 127–152) Counties.

675. Sanilac (ED 's 153–158), Schoolcraft, and Shiawassee Counties.

676. Tuscola and Van Buren (ED's 145–161) Counties.

677. Van Buren (ED's 162–175) and Washtenaw (ED's 111–143) Counties.

678. Washtenaw (ED's 144–152) and Wayne (ED's 1–3, 279–297, 327) Counties.

679. Wayne (ED's 4–22, 298–314) County.

680. Wayne (ED's 23–34, 245–266, 326) County.

681. Wayne (ED's 35–65, 319) County.

682. Wayne (ED's 66–96) County.

683. Wayne (ED's 97–134, 323, 324) County.

684. Wayne (ED's 135–157) County.

685. Wayne (ED's 158–187) County.

686. Wayne (ED's 188–217) County.

687. Wayne (ED's 218–244, 315, 317, 318, 322, 325, 328) County.

688. Wayne (ED's 267–278, 316, 320, 321) County.

MINNESOTA

689. Aitkin, Anoka, Cook, Becker, and Clearwater Counties.

690. Beltrami, Red Lake, Benton, Big Stone, and Blue Earth (ED's 1–6) Counties.

691. Blue Earth (ED's 7–34), Brown, and Carlton (ED's 31–35) Counties.

692. Carlton (ED's 36–43), Cottonwood, Carver, and Chisago (ED's 1–10) Counties.

693. Chisago (ED's 11–17), Clay, Cass, and Chippewa Counties.

694. Crow Wing, Douglas, and Meeker Counties.

695. Dakota, Dodge, and Freeborn (ED's 39–49) Counties.

696. Freeborn (ED's 50–61), Steele, Faribault, and Jackson (ED's 92–98) Counties.

697. Jackson (ED's 99–108), Marshall, and Fillmore Counties.

698. Goodhue and Le Sueur Counties.

699. Grant, Lyon, and Hennepin (ED's 1–16, 213–216, 221) Counties.

700. Hennepin (ED's 17–46) County.

701. Hennepin (ED's 47–78) County.

702. Hennepin (ED's 79–109) County.

703. Hennepin (ED's 110–142) County.

704. Hennepin (ED's 143–173) County.

705. Hennepin (ED's 174–201) County.

706. Hennepin (ED's 202–212, 217–220), Houston, and Hubbard Counties.

707. Isanti, Kanabec, Koochiching, Itasca, and Lake Counties.

708. Kandiyohi, McLeod, and Murray Counties.

709. Kittson, Lac qui Parle, Lincoln, and Nobles Counties.

710. Mahnomen, Norman, Pennington, Martin, and Sherburne Counties.

711. Mille Lacs, Pine, and Morrison Counties.

712. Mower, Nicollet, and Pope Counties.

713. Olmsted, Redwood, and Rock Counties.

714. Otter Tail County.

715. Pipestone, Stevens, Traverse, and Polk (ED's 183–211) Counties.

716. Polk (ED's 212–225), Swift, and Ramsey (ED's 18–21, 36–48) Counties.

717. Ramsey (ED's 22–35, 49–52, 62–70, 190) County.

718. Ramsey (ED's 53–61, 71–76, 126–142, 191) County.

719. Ramsey (ED's 77–89, 108–125, 192, 193) County.

720. Ramsey (ED's 90–107, 143–163) County.

721. Renville and Rice Counties.

722. Roseau, Scott, and St. Louis (ED's 129–143, 197–200) Counties.

723. St. Louis (ED's 201–226, 229–235) County.
724. St. Louis (ED's 144–153, 163–167, 180–183, 227, 228, 236–245) County.
725. St. Louis (ED's 154–162, 168–179, 184–196, 247, 248) County.
726. Sibley, Wilkin, and Stearns (ED's 129–148, 221) Counties.
727. Stearns (ED's 149–166), Todd, and Wright (ED's 199, 200) Counties.
728. Wright (ED's 201–220), Wabasha, and Winona (ED's 175–184) Counties.
729. Winona (ED's 185–207), Wadena, and Yellow Medicine Counties.
730. Waseca, Watonwan, and Washington Counties.

MISSISSIPPI

731. Adams, Alcorn, and Benton (ED's 1, 2, 5–8) Counties.
732. Benton (ED's 3, 4), Amite, and Attala Counties.
733. Bolivar County.
734. Calhoun, Issaquena, and Carroll Counties.
735. Chickasaw, Choctaw, and Claiborne Counties.
736. Clarke, Clay, and Coahoma (ED's 23–27) Counties.
737. Coahoma (ED's 28–38) and Copiah (ED's 42–55, 125) Counties.
738. Copiah (ED's 56–59, 126), Covington, and De Soto Counties.
739. Forrest, George, Franklin, and Hancock Counties.
740. Greene, Kemper, Grenada, and Harrison (ED's 31–35, 140) Counties.
741. Harrison (ED's 36–51) and Hinds (ED's 1–3, 5–11) Counties.
742. Hinds (ED's 4, 12–27) and Holmes (ED's 39–42, 46–48) Counties.
743. Holmes (ED's 43–45, 49–56), Itawamba, and Jackson (ED's 54–61, 139) Counties.
744. Jackson (ED's 62–65), Jasper, Jefferson, and Jefferson Davis (ED's 66–69) Counties.
745. Jefferson Davis (ED's 70–71), Lafayette, and Jones (ED's 72–81, 143) Counties.
746. Jones (ED's 82–84) and Lauderdale Counties.
747. Lamar, Lawrence, Leake, and Perry Counties.
748. Lee and Leflore (ED's 65–68, 72–75) Counties.
749. Leflore (ED's 69–71), Sharkey, and Lincoln Counties.
750. Lowndes and Madison (ED's 28–36) Counties.
751. Madison (ED's 37–41), Marion, and Marshall Counties.
752. Monroe and Montgomery Counties.
753. Neshoba, Pearl River, and Newton Counties.
754. Noxubee, Oktibbeha, and Panola (ED's 57–59) Counties.
755. Panola (ED's 53–56, 60–69, 119) and Pike (ED's 100–110, 128) Counties.
756. Pike (ED's 94–99), Webster, Pontotoc, and Prentiss (ED's 106–109) Counties.
757. Prentiss (ED's 110–115), Scott, Quitman, and Tippah Counties.
758. Rankin, Simpson, and Smith (ED's 107–111) Counties.
759. Smith (ED's 112–117), Tunica, and Sunflower Counties.
760. Tallahatchie, Tate, and Tishomingo (ED's 116, 117–119, 126) Counties.
761. Tishomingo (ED's 120–123), Union, and Warren (ED's 52–64, 97) Counties.
762. Warren (ED's 65–72), Wayne, and Washington (ED's 107–113, 121–127) Counties.
763. Washington (ED's 114–120, 128–133), Wilkinson, and Winston (ED's 118–121) Counties.
764. Winston (ED's 122–128), Yalobusha, and Yazoo (ED's 77–79, 88–95) Counties.
765. Yazoo (ED's 73–76, 80–87, 96) County.

MISSOURI

766. Adair, Andrew, and Atchison Counties.
767. Audrain, Barry, and Barton (ED's 19–24) Counties.
768. Barton (ED's 25–32, 162), Cedar, and Bates Counties.
769. Benton, Bollinger, and Butler Counties.
770. Boone and Cass Counties.
771. Buchanan (ED's 46–70, 90–102, 164) County.
772. Buchanan (ED's 31–45, 71–89, 163) and Camden Counties.
773. Caldwell, Douglas, and Cooper Counties.
774. Callaway and Cape Girardeau Counties.
775. Carroll, Carter, and Clay Counties.
776. Chariton, Christian, and Clark (ED's 24–34) Counties.
777. Clark (ED's 35–38), Cole, Clinton, and Dade (ED's 63–71) Counties.
778. Dade (ED's 72–77), Harrison, Crawford, and Dallas Counties.
779. Daviess, Hickory, De Kalb, and Dent Counties.
780. Dunklin and Franklin (ED's 43–59) Counties.
781. Franklin (ED's 60–68), Gentry, Gasconade, and Greene (ED's 16–18, 57–64) Counties.
782. Greene (ED's 19–56, 188, 189) County.
783. Grundy, Iron, and Henry Counties.
784. Holt, Howard, and Howell Counties.
785. Jackson (ED's 17–57) County.
786. Jackson (ED's 58–98) County.
787. Jackson (ED's 99–140) County.
788. Jackson (ED's 141–177) County.
789. Jackson (ED's 178–215) County.
790. Jackson (ED's 1–16, 216–218) and Jasper (ED's 35–49, 160) Counties.
791. Jasper (ED's 33, 34, 50–74, 80, 81) County.
792. Jasper (ED's 75–79, 82–84, 161), Lewis, and Jefferson Counties.
793. Johnson, Knox, and Laclede (ED's 36–46) Counties.
794. Laclede (ED's 47–50), Lafayette, and Lincoln Counties.
795. Lawrence and Linn Counties.
796. Livingston and Macon Counties.
797. McDonald, Madison, Maries, and Phelps Counties.
798. Marion and Polk Counties.
799. Mercer, Mississippi, Miller, and Monroe (ED's 114–122) Counties.
800. Monroe (ED's 123–132), Moniteau, Montgomery, and Pettis (ED's 109–117) Counties.
801. Pettis (ED's 118–140), Morgan, and St. Clair (ED's 123–136) Counties.
802. St. Clair (ED's 137–142), New Madrid, and Newton Counties.
803. Nodaway, Osage, and Pemiscot (ED's 142–146, 152, see also roll 804) Counties.
804. Oregon, Ozark, Pemiscot (ED's 147–151, see also roll 803), and Perry Counties.
805. Pike, Platte, and Ripley Counties.
806. Pulaski, Putnam, Ralls, and Ray (ED's 127–139) Counties.
807. Ray (ED's 140–144), Reynolds, Schuyler, and Randolph Counties.
808. St. Charles and St. Francois (ED's 79–82, 89–96) Counties.
809. St. Francois (ED's 83–88) and St. Louis (ED's 97–111, 122–132) Counties.
810. St. Louis (city) ED's 112–121) and Ste. Genevieve Counties.
811. St. Louis (city) (ED's 1–35, 467, 468, 470).
812. St. Louis (city) (ED's 36–66).
813. St. Louis (city) (ED's 67–106, 465, 469, 474, 475).
814. St. Louis (city) (ED's 107–122, 368–387, 459, 461, 462).
815. St. Louis (city) (ED's 123–153, 463, 479).
816. St. Louis (city) (ED's 154–202, 457, 464, 477, 478).
817. St. Louis (city) (ED's 203–218, 250–262, 458, 466, 473, 480).
818. St. Louis (city) (ED's 219–249, 419–422, 471).
819. St. Louis (city) (ED's 263–279, 423–437, 481).
820. St. Louis (city) (ED's 280–325, 476).
821. St. Louis (city) (ED's 326–367, 456, 460).
822. St. Louis (city) (ED's 388–418, 455, 472).
823. St. Louis (city) (ED's 438–454) and Saline (ED's 160–183) County.
824. Saline (ED's 184–187), Scotland, Shannon, Scott, and Stoddard (ED's 178–180) Counties.

825. Stoddard (ED's 175–177, 181–190), Shelby, and Stone Counties.
826. Sullivan, Texas, and Washington Counties.
827. Taney, Vernon, and Wayne Counties.
828. Warren, Webster, Worth, and Wright Counties.

MONTANA

829. Beaverhead, Carbon, Broadwater, and Custer Counties.
830. Cascade and Chouteau Counties.
831. Dawson, Deer Lodge, and Fergus Counties.
832. Flathead, Gallatin, Granite, and Jefferson Counties.
833. Lewis and Clark, Lincoln, Meagher, and Ravalli Counties.
834. Madison, Park, and Missoula Counties.
835. Powell, Teton, Rosebud, Sanders, and Sweet Grass Counties.
836. Silver Bow County.
837. Valley and Yellowstone Counties.

NEBRASKA

838. Adams, Antelope, Banner, Blaine, Boone, and Box Butte Counties.
839. Boyd, Burt, Brown, Butler, and Buffalo Counties.
840. Cass, Cedar, Chase, Cherry, Cheyenne, and Clay Counties.
841. Colfax, Dawes, Cuming, Dakota, and Custer Counties.
842. Dawson, Deuel, Dixon, Dundy, and Dodge Counties.
843. Douglas (ED's 1–46) County.
844. Douglas (ED's 47–93) County.
845. Douglas (ED's 94–125), Fillmore, and Frontier Counties.
846. Franklin, Furnas, Gage, and Garden Counties.
847. Garfield, Gosper, Grant, Greeley, Hall, Hamilton, Hayes, Harlan, and Hitchcock Counties.
848. Holt, Hooker, Howard, Keya Paha, Kimball, Jefferson, and Keith Counties.
849. Johnson, Kearney, Knox, and Lancaster (ED's 37–48) Counties.
850. Lancaster (ED's 49–108), Logan, and Loup Counties.
851. Lincoln, McPherson, Madison, Merrick, and Nance Counties.
852. Morrill, Nemaha, Nuckolls, Pawnee, Otoe, and Perkins Counties.
853. Phelps, Pierce, Platte, Polk, and Red Willow Counties.
854. Richardson, Rock, Saline, Sarpy, and Scotts Bluff Counties.
855. Saunders, Seward, Sioux, Sheridan, and Washington Counties.
856. Sherman, Webster, Stanton, Valley, Thayer, Thomas, and Wheeler Counties.
857. Thurston, Wayne, and York Counties.

NEVADA

858. Churchill, Clark, Douglas, Elko, Lincoln, Esmeralda, Eureka, Humboldt, and Lander Counties.
859. Lyon, Nye, Ormsby, White Pine, Storey, and Washoe Counties.

NEW HAMPSHIRE

860. Belknap, Carroll, and Cheshire (ED's 30–42) Counties.
861. Cheshire (ED's 43–50), Coos, and Grafton (ED's 72–89, 321) Counties.
862. Grafton (ED's 90-105) and Hillsborough (ED's 106–134) Counties.
863. Hillsborough (ED's 135–157, 160–171) County.
864. Hillsborough (ED's 158, 159, 172–182) and Merrimack (ED's 183–216, 320) Counties.
865. Merrimack (ED's 217–231) and Rockingham (ED's 232–260) Counties.
866. Rockingham (ED's 261–274), Strafford, and Sullivan Counties.

NEW JERSEY

867. Atlantic County.
868. Bergen (ED's 1–21) County.
869. Bergen (ED's 22–46) County.
870. Bergen (ED's 47–57) and Cape May Counties.
871. Burlington (ED's 40–73) County.
872. Burlington (ED's 74–84) and Camden (ED's 1–25, 90–101) Counties.

873. Camden (ED's 26–58, 66–71, 164) County.
874. Camden (ED's 59–65, 72–89, 102–115) County.
875. Cumberland County.
876. Essex (ED's 1–21, 236) County.
877. Essex (ED's 22–39, 72–78, 240) County.
878. Essex (ED's 40–71, 99, 100) County.
879. Essex (ED's 101–105, 114–126, 233, 234, 243) County.
880. Essex (ED's 79–98, 127–134, 232, 237, 238, 242) County.
881. Essex (ED's 106–113, 135–144, 201–203) County.
882. Essex (ED's 145–163, 179–187, 229, 230) County.
883. Essex (ED's 164–178, 188–200, 235, 241) County.
884. Essex (ED's 204–228, 231, 239) County.
885. Gloucester and Hudson (ED's 35–42) Counties.
886. Hudson (ED's 1–30) County.
887. Hudson (ED's 31–34, 43–47, 69–77, 229–243) County.
888. Hudson (ED's 48–68, 78–82) County.
889. Hudson (ED's 83–107) County.
890. Hudson (ED's 108–149, 300) County.
891. Hudson (ED's 150–169, 186–198) County.
892. Hudson (ED's 170–185, 199–213) County.
893. Hudson (ED's 214–228, 244–251, 268–273) County.
894. Hudson (ED's 252–267, 274–299) County.
895. Hunterdon and Mercer (ED's 29–39, 104) Counties.
896. Mercer (ED's 40–66, 73–75, 105, 106, 126, 128) County.
897. Mercer (ED's 67–72, 76–103) County.
898. Middlesex (ED's 1–23, 45–48, 51, 52, 137) County.
899. Middlesex (ED's 24–44, 49, 50) County.
900. Middlesex (ED's 53–55) and Monmouth (ED's 56–76, 79–85) Counties.
901. Monmouth (ED's 77, 78, 86–117) County.
902. Morris (ED's 1–32) County.
903. Morris (ED's 33–49) and Ocean Counties.
904. Passaic (ED's 58–69, 75–78, 159–161, 191, 192) County.
905. Passaic (ED's 70–74, 79–92, 104–110, 193, 194) County.
906. Passaic (ED's 93–103, 111–140, 153–158) County.
907. Passaic (ED's 141–152, 162–167) and Somerset (ED's 107–112) Counties.
908. Somerset (ED's 113–125, 127, 129) and Salem Counties.
909. Sussex and Union (ED's 50–70) Counties.
910. Union (ED's 71–100, 155) County.
911. Union (ED's 101–120) and Warren (ED's 121–134) Counties.
912. Warren (ED's 135–154) County.

NEW MEXICO

913. Bernalillo, Chaves, and Colfax Counties.
914. Curry, Dona Ana, Eddy, and Guadalupe Counties.
915. Grant, Lincoln, Luna, and McKinley Counties.
916. Mora, Otero, Quay, and Rio Arriba Counties.
917. Roosevelt, San Juan, and San Miguel Counties.
918. Sandoval, Santa Fe, Sierra, and Socorro Counties.
919. Taos, Torrance, Union, and Valencia Counties.

NEW YORK

920. Albany (ED's 1–49, 226) County.
921. Albany (ED's 50–98) County.
922. Albany (ED's 99–137, 141) County.
923. Albany (ED's 138–140, 142–162, 225) and Allegany (ED's 1–28) Counties.
924. Allegany (ED's 29–42) and Chenango Counties.
925. Broome (ED's 1–39, 42) County.
926. Broome (ED's 40, 41, 43–66) and Cattaraugus (ED's 43–69) Counties.
927. Cattaraugus (ED's 70–102, 196) and Cayuga (ED's 31–46) Counties.
928. Cayuga (ED's 1–30, 47–71) County.

929. Chautauqua (ED's 103–143, 152–155) County.

930. Chautauqua (ED's 144–151, 156–195) County.

931. Chemung County.

932. Clinton County.

933. Columbia and Essex (ED's 39–46) Counties.

934. Essex (ED's 47–68) and Cortland Counties.

935. Delaware and Hamilton Counties.

936. Dutchess (ED's 34–55, 61–74) County.

937. Dutchess (ED's 56–60, 75–89) and Franklin (ED's 69–83) Counties.

938. Franklin (ED's 84–109) and Erie (ED's 240–247, 251–257, 268, 269) Counties.

939. Erie (ED's 248–250, 258–267, 270–290) County.

940. Erie (ED's 1–14, 291–309) County.

941. Erie (ED's 15–47) County.

942. Erie (ED's 48–75) County.

943. Erie (ED's 76–103) County.

944. Erie (ED's 104–130) County.

945. Erie (ED's 131–164) County.

946. Erie (ED's 165–192, 310) County.

947. Erie (ED's 193–216, 223, 230) County.

948. Erie (ED's 217–222, 231–239) and Fulton (ED's 1–23, 39, 40) Counties.

949. Fulton (ED's 24–38) and Otsego (ED's 41–65, 76, 187) Counties.

950. Otsego (ED's 66–75, 77–83) and Greene Counties.

951. Genesee and Herkimer (ED's 1–12, 18) Counties.

952. Herkimer (ED's 13–17, 19–41), and Rockland (ED's 93–104, 123–125, 158) Counties.

953. Rockland (ED's 105–122, 160) and Jefferson (ED's 1–21, 31–33) Counties.

954. Jefferson (ED's 22–30, 34–71) County.

955. Kings (ED's 1–40) County.

956. Kings (ED's 41–73) County.

957. Kings (ED's 74–81, 83–90, 92–98, 100–114) County.

958. Kings (ED's 115–146, 148) County.

959. Kings (ED's 147, 149–161, 222–238) County.

960. Kings (ED's 162–195) County.

961. Kings (ED's 196–221, 260–264, 266) County.

962. Kings (ED's 265, 267–296) County.

963. Kings (ED's 239–259, 297–311) County.

964. Kings (ED's 312–343) County.

965. Kings (ED's 344–377) County.

966. Kings (ED's 378–412) County.

967. Kings (ED's 413–444) County.

968. Kings (ED's 445–458, 476–493, 495) County.

969. Kings (ED's 494, 496–522) County.

970. Kings (ED's 82, 91, 99, 459–475, 523–541) County.

971. Kings (ED's 542–576) County.

972. Kings (ED's 577–612) County.

973. Kings (ED's 613–620, 683–705) County.

974. Kings (ED's 621–639, 706–725) County.

975. Kings (ED's 640–682) County.

976. Kings (ED's 726–757, 1403) County.

977. Kings (ED's 758–761, 763–792) County.

978. Kings (ED's 793–810, 965–967) County.

979. Kings (ED's 811–824, 828–832, 968–986) County.

980. Kings (ED's 825–827, 833–865) County.

981. Kings (ED's 866–903) County.

982. Kings (ED's 904–939) County.

983. Kings (ED's 940–955, 957–959, 961–964, 991–995, 1003–1006, 1009, 1012–1028, 1064, 1065, 1404, 1405) County.

984. Kings (ED's 1007, 1029–1063, 1406–1408) County.

985. Kings (ED's 987–990, 996–1002, 1008, 1010, 1011, 1066–1102, 1409–1413) County.

986. Lewis and Livingston (ED's 36–47, 50–58) Counties.

987. Livingston (ED's 48, 49, 59–68) and Madison Counties.

988. Monroe (ED's 1–38) County.

989. Monroe (ED's 39–68, 93–98, 100–107, 224, 228) County.

990. Monroe (ED's 69–82, 171–201, 229) County.

991. Monroe (ED's 83–92, 108–117, 135–145, 153–158, 225, 227) County.

992. Monroe (ED's 118–134, 146–152, 159–170, 210–213, 226) County.

993. Monroe (ED's 99, 202–209, 214–222) and Montgomery (ED's 49–59, 62–68) Counties.

994. Montgomery (ED's 60, 61, 69–94) and Nassau (ED's 1103–1114, 1117) Counties.

995. Nassau (ED's 1115, 1116, 1118–1144) County.

996. New York (ED's 1397–1419, 1421–1426, 1728, 1744) County.

997. New York (ED's 1017, 1275, 1428–1430, 1432–1457, 1463, 1746) County.

998. New York (ED's 1458–1462, 1464–1490, 1714, 1739) County.

999. New York (ED's 690, 1274, 1427, 1491–1513) County.

1000. New York (ED's 1514–1518, 1520–1545, 1647, 1648, 1718, 1719, 1721) County.

1001. New York (ED's 1546–1574, 1715) County.

1002. New York (ED's 1575–1605, 1645, 1646, 1649, 1720, 1729) County.

1003. New York (ED's 701, 1606–1642) County.

1004. New York (ED's 1–13, 30–36, 103–125) County.

1005. New York (ED's 14–27, 29, 37–42, 44–51, 126–133, 180, 682, 1705) County.

1006. New York (ED's 134–177) County.

1007. New York (ED's 28, 52–77, 563, 1519, 1685, 1686, 1691, 1692) County.

1008. New York (ED's 78–102, 1687–1690, 1693, 1694) County.

1009. New York (ED's 178, 181–211) County.

1010. New York (ED's 212–236, 1695, 1704) County.

1011. New York (ED's 237–254, 1657, 1658, 1663–1667, 1696–1698) County.

1012. New York (ED's 255–271, 1655, 1656, 1659–1662, 1668–1673) County.

1013. New York (ED's 272–275, 280–305, 437, 1734) County.

1014. New York (ED's 306–331) County.

1015. New York (ED's 332–351, 1722) County.

1016. New York (ED's 352–370, 372, 374, 376, 378–380, 1654) County.

1017. New York (ED's 381, 382, 385–412) County.

1018. New York (ED's 413–436, 438–445) County.

1019. New York (ED's 446–473, 1139) County.

1020. New York (ED's 474–483, 485–496, 499–502, 507, 517, 519) County.

1021. New York (ED's 503, 504, 508–516, 518, 520–531, 1716, 1717, 1732) County.

1022. New York (ED's 532–539, 542, 543, 545–550, 552–562, 564–569, 1738) County.

1023. New York (ED's 570–601, 1731) County.

1024. New York (ED's 602–624, 626–635, 1730) County.

1025. New York (ED's 636–646, 648, 649, 651–671, 704) County.

1026. New York (ED's 672–681, 683–689, 691–700, 702, 1733, 1742) County.

1027. New York (ED's 703, 705–730, 1420, 1431, 1644) County.

1028. New York (ED's 731–761, 1653) County.

1029. New York (ED's 762–791) County.

1030. New York (ED's 792–823) County.

1031. New York (ED's 824–827, 868–885, 1674, 1675, 1682, 1699–1701) County.

1032. New York (ED's 886–907, 1702, 1703) County.

1033. New York (ED's 908–926, 1003, 1010, 1055, 1060, 1071, 1164, 1676–1681, 1683) County.

1034. New York (ED's 828–848, 927–938, 1002, 1078, 1684) County.

1035. New York (ED's 43, 849–867, 939–953, 1706, 1707) County.

1036. New York (ED's 544, 551, 625, 650, 954–985, 988–993, 995, 1710–1713) County.

1037. New York (ED's 986, 987, 994, 996, 1119–1122, 1170–1174, 1241–1270, 1708, 1709) County.

1038. New York (ED's 276–279, 371, 373, 375, 377, 383, 384, 484, 997–1001, 1004–1009, 1011–1014, 1727, 1735–1737) County.

1039. New York (ED's 1015, 1016, 1018–1041, 1118, 1643) County.

1040. New York (ED's 1042–1054, 1056–1059, 1061–1067, 1069, 1070, 1072) County.

1041. New York (ED's 541, 647, 1073–1077, 1079–1109, 1743) County.

1042. New York (ED's 497, 498, 1068, 1110–1117, 1123–1138, 1140, 1142–1157) County.

1043. New York (ED's 505, 540, 1141, 1158–1163, 1165–1169, 1175–1197, 1201, 1206, 1207, 1741) County.

1044. New York (ED's 1198, 1208–1224, 1226–1238, 1725, 1745) County.

1045. New York (ED's 1199, 1200, 1202–1205, 1239, 1240, 1271–1273, 1276–1304, 1724) County.

1046. New York (ED's 1305–1338, 1726) County.

1047. New York (ED's 1339–1366, 1723) County.

1048. New York (ED's 1367–1396, 1650–1652, 1740, 1747, 1748) County.

1049. Niagara (ED's 69–95, 111, 119–131) County.

1050. Niagara (ED's 96–110, 112–118, 132–142, 198) and Putnam Counties.

1051. Oneida (ED's 42–72, 77–95) County.

1052. Oneida (ED's 73–76, 96–113, 116–133, 153–155) County.

1053. Oneida (ED's 114, 115, 134–152, 156–182) County.

1054. Onondaga (ED's 39–85) County.

1055. Onondaga (ED's 86–104, 110–120, 137–142, 196–200) County.

1056. Onondaga (ED's 105–109, 121–136, 143–147, 166–176) County.

1057. Onondaga (ED's 148–165, 177–195) County.

1058. Ontario County.

1059. Orange (ED's 1–42) County.

1060. Orange (ED's 43–83) County.

1061. Orange (ED's 84–92), Schuyler, and Orleans (ED's 143–163) Counties.

1062. Orleans (ED's 164–168) and Oswego (ED's 101–119, 127–147) Counties.

1063. Oswego (ED's 120–126, 148–164) and Queens (ED's 1145–1159) Counties.

1064. Queens (ED's 1160–1176, 1253–1262) County.

1065. Queens (ED's 1263–1290) County.

1066. Queens (ED's 1177–1201, 1252) County.

1067. Queens (ED's 1202–1225) County.

1068. Queens (ED's 1226–1251) County.

1069. Rensselaer (ED's 1–22, 34–36) County.

1070. Rensselaer (ED's 42–63, 76–78) County.

1071. Rensselaer (ED's 23–33, 37–41, 64–75, 79, 80) and Sullivan (ED's 126–132) Counties.

1072. Sullivan (ED's 133–157, 159) and Richmond (ED's 1291–1303, 1328, 1335, 1337) Counties.

1073. Richmond (ED's 1304–1327, 1329–1334, 1336) County.

1074. St. Lawrence (ED's 110–141, 145–148, 169–175) County.

1075. St. Lawrence (ED's 142–144, 149–168, 176–181) and Yates Counties.

1076. Saratoga (ED's 95–137, 148) County.

1077. Saratoga (ED's 138–147) and Schenectady (ED's 163–188) Counties.

1078. Schenectady (ED's 189–224) County.

1079. Schoharie and Steuben (ED's 91–104, 112–123) Counties.

1080. Steuben (ED's 105–111, 124–168) County.

1081. Seneca and Suffolk (ED's 1338–1356) Counties.

1082. Suffolk (ED's 1357–1360, 1369–1377, 1383–1402) County.

1083. Suffolk (ED's 1361–1368, 1378–1382) and Tompkins Counties.

1084. Tioga and Ulster (ED's 114–123, 145–153, 185, 186) Counties.

1085. Ulster (ED's 124–144, 154–171) County.

1086. Ulster (ED's 172–184), Warren, and Wyoming (ED's 169–174) Counties.

1087. Wyoming (ED's 175–197) and Washington (ED's 81–103) Counties.

1088. Washington (ED's 104–122) and Westchester (ED's 1–4, 19–21, 40–45, 190–192) Counties.

1089. Westchester (ED's 5–18, 22–39, 97, 98, 111, 193, 194) County.

1090. Westchester (ED's 46–52, 58–76, 99–109, 195–197) County.

1091. Westchester (ED's 53–57, 77–96, 127–137) County.

1092. Westchester (ED's 110, 112–126, 138–148, 162–168) County.

1093. Westchester (ED's 149–161, 169–189) County.

1094. Wayne County.

NORTH CAROLINA

1095. Alamance, Alexander, and Carteret Counties.

1096. Alleghany, Ashe, and Anson Counties.

1097. Beaufort and Bladen Counties.

1098. Bertie, Brunswick, and Chowan Counties.

1099. Buncombe and Clay Counties.

1100. Burke, Dare, and Cabarrus Counties.

1101. Caldwell, Camden, Caswell, and Gates Counties.

1102. Catawba, Chatham, and Cleveland (ED's 33–35) Counties.

1103. Cleveland (ED's 36–51), Cherokee, and Perquimans Counties.

1104. Columbus and Craven Counties.

1105. Cumberland and Martin Counties.

1106. Currituck, Person, and Davidson (ED's 17–32, 35) Counties.

1107. Davidson (ED's 33, 34), Madison, Davie, and Greene Counties.

1108. Duplin and Durham (ED's 30–41, 192) Counties.

1109. Durham (ED's 29, 42–46), Mitchell, and Edgecombe (ED's 13–25, 28, 29) Counties.

1110. Edgecombe (ED's 26, 27), Richmond, and Forsyth (ED's 47–64) Counties.

1111. Forsyth (ED's 65–75) and Franklin Counties.

1112. Gaston and McDowell Counties.

1113. Graham, Haywood, and Granville Counties.

1114. Guilford (ED's 91–121, 124–126, 193) County.

1115. Guilford (ED's 122, 123, 127–130), Henderson, and Halifax (ED's 40–54) Counties.

1116. Halifax (ED's 55–58), Jackson, Harnett, and Tyrrell Counties.

1117. Hertford, Pamlico, Hyde, and Lincoln Counties.

1118. Iredell and Johnston (ED's 34–44) Counties.

1119. Johnston (ED's 45–60), Jones, and Moore Counties.

1120. Lee, Watauga, and Lenoir Counties.

1121. Macon, Onslow, and Mecklenburg (ED's 93–107) Counties.

1122. Mecklenburg (ED's 108–137, 162) and Yancey Counties.

1123. Montgomery, Swain, and Nash (ED's 61–74, 78) Counties.

1124. Nash (ED's 75–77), Pasquotank, and New Hanover (ED's 82–96, 129) Counties.

1125. New Hanover (ED's 78–81), Stanly, Northampton, and Pender (ED's 69–71) Counties.

1126. Pender (ED's 72–78), Orange, and Pitt (ED's 87–97, 102, 103) Counties.

1127. Pitt (ED's 98–101), Scotland, Polk, and Vance Counties.

1128. Randolph and Stokes Counties.

1129. Robeson County.

1130. Rockingham and Yadkin Counties.

1131. Rowan and Washington Counties.

1132. Rutherford and Sampson (ED's 79–94) Counties.

1133. Sampson (ED's 95–97), Warren, and Surry (ED's 126–141) Counties.

1134. Surry (ED's 142–144), Transylvania, Union, and Wilkes (ED's 160, 161, 163–165) Counties.

1135. Wilkes (ED's 162, 166–182) and Wake (ED's 92–108) Counties.

1136. Wake (ED's 109–134) and Wayne (ED's 98–102, 118) Counties.

1137. Wayne (ED's 103–117) and Wilson Counties.

NORTH DAKOTA

1138. Adams, Barnes, Benson, and Billings Counties.

1139. Bowman, Richland, Bottineau, and Burke Counties.

1140. Burleigh, Divide, Dunn, and Cass (ED's 27–35, 38–46) Counties.

1141. Cass (ED's 36, 37, 47–51), Cavalier, Dickey, Eddy, and Emmons Counties.

1142. Foster, Griggs, Hettinger, Kidder, and Grand Forks Counties.

1143. La Moure, Logan, Mountrail, McHenry, and McIntosh Counties.

1144. McKenzie, McLean, Mercer, and Morton Counties.

1145. Nelson, Pembina, Oliver, and Walsh Counties.

1146. Pierce, Ramsey, Ransom, Renville, and Sheridan Counties.

1147. Rolette and Stutsman Counties.

1148. Sargent, Steele, Towner, Stark, and Traill Counties.

1149. Ward, Wells, and Williams Counties.

OHIO

1150. Adams and Allen (ED's 1–18, 41–44) Counties.

1151. Allen (ED's 19–40, 45–48) and Ashland Counties.

1152. Ashtabula (ED's 1–43, 248) County.

1153. Ashtabula (ED's 44–50) and Athens Counties.

1154. Auglaize and Butler (ED's 1, 10–13, 21–27, 36) Counties.

1155. Butler (ED's 2–9, 14–20, 28–35, 37–44) County.

1156. Belmont (ED's 1–7, 10–36, 168, 169) County.

1157. Belmont (ED's 8, 9, 37–51, 53–55) and Brown Counties.

1158. Carroll and Clark (ED's 1–15, 28–46) Counties.

1159. Clark (ED's 16–27, 47–57) and Champaign Counties.

1160. Clermont and Clinton Counties.

1161. Columbiana (ED's 1–46) County.

1162. Columbiana (ED's 47–70) and Coshocton (ED's 1–15, 18–28) Counties.

1163. Coshocton (ED's 16, 17, 29, 30), Crawford, and Darke (ED's 72–76, 80–89) Counties.

1164. Darke (ED's 77–79, 90–106) and Cuyahoga (ED's 1–11, 18–20, 23–25, 433, 435) Counties.

1165. Cuyahoga (ED's 12–17, 21, 22, 26–48, 413, 434, 436) County.

1166. Cuyahoga (ED's 49–79, 94, 95, 97, 422) County.

1167. Cuyahoga (ED's 96, 98–115, 124, 137–148, 416, 427) County.

1168. Cuyahoga (ED's 80–93, 116–123, 125–134, 149–153, 424) County.

1169. Cuyahoga (ED's 135, 136, 154–187, 426) County.

1170. Cuyahoga (ED's 188–221) County.

1171. Cuyahoga (ED's 222–237, 302–314, 420) County.

1172. Cuyahoga (ED's 238–265, 418, 419, 421, 425) County.

1173. Cuyahoga (ED's 266–285, 287–297, 301, 415, 423, 431, 432) County.

1174. Cuyahoga (ED's 286, 298–300, 315–322, 324–329, 331–337, 339–341, 343, 344, 428) County.

1175. Cuyahoga (ED's 323, 330, 338, 342, 345–374, 417, 430) County.

1176. Cuyahoga (ED's 375–412, 414, 429, 437) County.

1177. Defiance and Delaware Counties.

1178. Erie and Fairfield (ED's 48–59, 72) Counties.

1179. Fairfield (ED's 60–71, 73–80), Fayette, and Franklin (ED's 1–3, 16) Counties.

1180. Franklin (ED's 20–24, 27–64, 66) County. 2081181.

      Franklin (ED's 25, 26, 65, 67–117) County.

1182. Franklin (ED's 9–11, 118–162) County.

1183. Franklin (ED's 4–8, 12–15, 17–19, 163–197, 200, 201) County.

1184. Franklin (ED's 198, 199), Fulton, and Gallia Counties.

1185. Geauga, Greene, and Guernsey (ED's 15–17) Counties.

1186. Guernsey (ED's 1–14, 18–36) and Hancock (ED's 58–64, 77–83) Counties.

1187. Hancock (ED's 65–76, 84–89) and Hardin Counties.

1188. Hamilton (ED's 1–27, 58–62, 375) County.

1189. Hamilton (ED's 38–57, 63–66, 147–160, 377) County.

1190. Hamilton (ED's 67–90, 102–110, 161–170, 374) County.

1191. Hamilton (ED's 91–101, 111–139, 373) County.

1192. Hamilton (ED's 140–146, 171–199, 378) County.

1193. Hamilton (ED's 200–241, 372) County.

1194. Hamilton (ED's 242–284) County.

1195. Hamilton (ED's 285–326) County.

1196. Hamilton (ED's 327–371) County.

1197. Harrison, Highland, and Jackson (ED's 49–52) Counties.

1198. Jackson (ED's 53–76) and Henry Counties.

1199. Hocking and Knox Counties.

1200. Holmes and Huron Counties.

1201. Jefferson (ED's 93–117, 121–135, 140, 141) County.

1202. Jefferson (ED's 118–120, 136–139, 142–144) and Lawrence Counties.

1203. Lake and Licking (ED's 47–68, 96–102) Counties.

1204. Licking (ED's 69–95) and Logan (ED's 120–143, 146, 147, 149) Counties.

1205. Logan (ED's 144, 145, 148), Medina, and Lorain (ED's 81–86, 90–92, 96–98, 208, 211, 212) Counties.

1206. Lorain (ED's 87–89, 93–95, 99–127, 209, 210) County.

1207. Lucas (ED's 19–45, 84–98) County.

1208. Lucas (ED's 46–75, 150–157) County.

1209. Lucas (ED's 76–83, 99–131) County.

1210. Lucas (ED's 132–149, 158–163) and Madison Counties.

1211. Mahoning (ED's 71–84, 87–90, 96–105, 139–145) County.

1212. Mahoning (ED's 106–132, 146–148) County.

1213. Mahoning (ED's 85, 86, 91–95, 133–138) and Marion Counties.

1214. Meigs and Mercer Counties.

1215. Miami and Montgomery (ED's 45–47, 152) Counties.

1216. Montgomery (ED's 48–74, 93–99) County.

1217. Montgomery (ED's 75–92, 100–117) County.

1218. Montgomery (ED's 118–151) County.

1219. Monroe, Morgan, and Morrow (ED's 146–155) Counties.

1220. Morrow (ED's 156–162), Ottawa, and Paulding Counties.

1221. Muskingum (ED's 54–75, 77–80, 87–107) County.

1222. Muskingum (ED's 76, 81–86), Noble, and Perry (ED's 121–138) Counties.

1223. Perry (ED's 139–146), Pike, and Pickaway Counties.

1224. Portage and Richland (ED's 163–169, 194–207) Counties.

1225. Richland (ED's 170–193), Preble, and Putnam (ED's 67, 68) Counties.

1226. Putnam (ED's 69–89, 138) and Ross (ED's 147–154, 165–177) Counties.

1227. Ross (ED's 155–164, 178–183) and Sandusky Counties.

1228. Scioto and Seneca (ED's 135–137) Counties.

1229. Seneca (ED's 138–173) and Vinton Counties.

1230. Shelby and Stark (ED's 153–171) Counties.

1231. Stark (ED's 149–152, 172–192, 218–232) County.

1232. Stark (ED's 193–217, 233–245) and Summit (ED's 172, 173, 175, 176) Counties.

1233. Summit (ED's 119–157) County.

1234. Summit (ED's 158–171, 174, 177–202, 249, 250) County.

1235. Trumbull County.

1236. Tuscarawas (ED's 103–149) County.

1237. Tuscarawas (ED's 150–155) and Washington Counties.

1238. Union and Van Wert Counties.

1239. Warren and Wayne (ED's 156–169, 171–179) Counties.

1240. Wayne (ED's 170, 180–191) and Wood (ED's 178–207, 209) Counties.

1241. Wood (ED's 208, 210–212), Wyandot, and Williams Counties.

OKLAHOMA

1242. Adair, Alfalfa, Atoka, and Beaver Counties.

1243. Beckham, Blaine, and Bryan (ED's 13–18) Counties.

1244. Bryan (ED's 19–34), Cherokee, and Caddo (ED's 46, 47) Counties.

1245. Caddo (ED's 48–70) and Cleveland Counties.

1246. Canadian and Carter Counties.

1247. Choctaw, Cimarron, Coal, and Comanche (ED's 35–37, 40) Counties.

1248. Comanche (ED's 38, 39, 41–69) and Craig (ED's 24–27) Counties.

1249. Craig (ED's 28–37), Harper, and Creek Counties.

1250. Custer, Delaware, and Dewey Counties.

1251. Ellis and Garfield Counties.

1252. Garvin and Grady (ED's 89–106) Counties.

1253. Grady (ED's 107–111), Grant, Greer, and Harmon Counties.

1254. Haskell, Jefferson, and Johnston Counties.

1255. Hughes and Jackson Counties.

1256. Kingfisher and Kay (ED's 52–66) Counties.

1257. Kay (ED's 67–71), Kiowa, and Latimer (ED's 132–140) Counties.

1258. Latimer (ED's 141–144), Le Flore, and Lincoln (ED's 88–90) Counties.

1259. Lincoln (ED's 91–116) and Logan (ED's 117–120, 137, 141) County.

1260. Logan (ED's 121–136, 138–140, 142) and McIntosh Counties.

1261. Love, McClain, and McCurtain Counties.

1262. Major, Marshall, Mayes, and Murray (ED's 200–202) Counties.

1263. Murray (ED's 203–209) and Muskogee (ED's 92–112, 121–124) Counties.

1264. Muskogee (ED's 113–120), Noble, and Nowata (ED's 125–129, 132, 133) Counties.

1265. Nowata (ED's 130, 131), Okfuskee, and Oklahoma (ED's 180–182, 184–203, 230–232) Counties.

1266. Oklahoma (ED's 204–229) County.

1267. Oklahoma (ED's 183, 296), Okmulgee, and Ottawa (ED's 157–166) Counties.

1268. Ottawa (ED 167), Pawnee, and Osage Counties.

1269. Payne and Pittsburg (ED's 210–225, 244, 245) Counties.

1270. Pittsburg (ED's 226–243) and Pontotoc Counties.

1271. Pottawatomie and Pushmataha Counties.

1272. Roger Mills and Sequoyah (ED's 193–209, 211) Counties.

1273. Sequoyah (ED 210), Texas, and Rogers Counties.

1274. Seminole and Tulsa (ED's 212–215, 219–233) Counties.

1275. Tulsa (ED's 216–218), Stephens, Tillman, and Washington (ED's 251–253) Counties.

1276. Washington (ED's 254–259), Woods, and Woodward Counties.

1277. Wagoner and Washita Counties.

OREGON

1278. Baker, Hood River, Benton, and Clatsop Counties.

1279. Clackamas, Columbia, and Crook Counties.

1280. Coos, Grant, Curry, Douglas, and Gilliam Counties.

1281. Harney, Josephine, Lincoln, and Jackson Counties.

1282. Klamath, Lake, Polk, and Lane (ED's 142–162, 304) Counties.

1283. Lane (ED's 163–165, 306, 309–312), Malheur, Tillamook, Linn, and Wheeler Counties.

1284. Marion, Morrow, and Wallowa Counties.

1285. Multnomah (ED's 124–142, 169–173, 319) County.

1286. Multnomah (ED's 143–168, 188–198) County.

1287. Multnomah (ED's 199–210, 227–242, 243(pt.), 246, 321, 327) County.

1288. Multnomah (ED's 110–123, 174–187, 243(pt.), 244–245, 320, 329) County.

1289. Multnomah (ED's 211–226), Sherman, and Umatilla Counties.

1290. Union, Wasco, and Yamhill (ED's 283–287, 289–297, 299) Counties.

1291. Yamhill (ED's 288, 298, 300, 301, 305) and Washington Counties.

PENNSYLVANIA

1292. Adams and Allegheny (ED's 1–16, 30–35) Counties.

1293. Allegheny (ED's 17–29, 36–64) County.

1294. Allegheny (ED's 65–108) County.

1295. Allegheny (ED's 109–158, 658) County.

1296. Allegheny (ED's 159–207) County.

1297. Allegheny (ED's 208–249, 252, 253) County.

1298. Allegheny (ED's 250, 251, 254–283, 659) County.

1299. Allegheny (ED's 284–315) County.

1300. Allegheny (ED's 316–346) County.

1301. Allegheny (ED's 347–379) County.

1302. Allegheny (ED's 380–422) County.

1303. Allegheny (ED's 423–458) County.

1304. Allegheny (ED's 459–496) County.

1305. Allegheny (ED's 497–525, 547–552) County.

1306. Allegheny (ED's 553–564, 581–603) County.

1307. Allegheny (ED's 526–546, 565–580, 604–620) County.

1308. Allegheny (ED's 621–657) County.

1309. Armstrong (ED's 1–36) County.

1310. Armstrong (ED's 37–53) and Beaver (ED's 1–22, 31) Counties.

1311. Beaver (ED's 23–30, 32–55) and Bedford (ED's 1–4, 7, 8) Counties.

1312. Bedford (ED's 5, 6, 9–32) and Berks (ED's 1–13, 16, 17) Counties.

1313. Berks (ED's 14, 15, 18–50, 211) County.

1314. Berks (ED's 51–85) County.

1315. Berks (ED's 86–119) County.

1316. Berks (ED's 120–130) and Blair (ED's 33–46, 60–67) Counties.

1317. Blair (ED's 47–59, 68–79) County.

1318. Blair (ED's 80–91) and Bradford (ED's 1–26, 28–31) Counties.

1319. Bradford (ED's 27, 32–56) and Bucks (ED's 1–19) Counties.

1320. Bucks (ED's 20–61) County.

1321. Butler (ED's 56–91, 256, 257) County.

1322. Butler (ED's 92–108) and Cambria (ED's 92–105) Counties.

1323. Cambria (ED's 106–116, 118–130, 132, 133) County.

1324. Cambria (ED's 117, 131, 134–151, 162, 163) County.

1325. Cambria (ED's 152–161), Cameron, and Center (ED's 7–23, 141, 142) Counties.

1326. Center (ED's 24–45) and Carbon (ED's 1–13, 17, 18) Counties.

1327. Carbon (ED's 14–16, 19–32) and Chester (ED's 1–21) Counties.

1328. Chester (ED's 22–63) County.

1329. Chester (ED's 64–90, 169) and Clarion (ED's 1–16) Counties.

1330. Clarion (ED's 17–32) and Clearfield (ED's 46–65, 68, 69) Counties.

1331. Clearfield (ED's 66, 67, 70–97, 103) County.

1332. Clearfield (ED's 98–102, 104, 105), Clinton, and Crawford (ED's 1–10) Counties.

1333. Crawford (ED's 11–56, 194) County.

1334. Columbia and Cumberland (ED's 1, 10–12) Counties.

1335. Cumberland (ED's 2–9, 13–43, 174) County.

1336. Dauphin (ED's 51–88) County.

1337. Dauphin (ED's 44–50, 89–114, 173) County.

1338. Dauphin (ED's 115–130, 132–134) and Delaware (ED's 91–103, 106–108) Counties.

1339. Delaware (ED's 104, 105, 109–138, 140–142) County.

1340. Delaware (ED's 139, 143–168, 170, 171) County.

1341. Elk and Erie (ED's 57–66, 107–109, 113, 114) Counties.

1342. Erie (ED's 67–99, 192) County.

1343. Erie (ED's 100–106, 110–112, 115–140) and Fayette (ED's 1–3) Counties.

1344. Fayette (ED's 4–45) County.

1345. Fayette (ED's 30–41, 46–58, 77) County.

1346. Fayette (ED's 59–76, 78–84, 87, 90, 91) County.

1347. Fayette (ED's 85, 86, 88, 89), Forest, and Franklin (ED's 1–23, 29, 30) Counties.

1348. Franklin (ED's 24–28, 31–43), Fulton, and Greene (ED's 92–111) Counties.

1349. Greene (ED's 112–125) and Huntingdon (ED's 55–89) Counties.

1350. Indiana (ED's 54–88, 91) County.

1351. Indiana (ED's 89, 90, 92–101) and Jefferson (ED's 62–84) Counties.

1352. Jefferson (ED's 85–103), Juniata, and Lancaster (ED's 1–8, 13, 23, 24) Counties.

1353. Lancaster (ED's 9–12, 14–22, 25–55, 58, 59) County.

1354. Lancaster (ED's 56, 57, 60–99, 149) County.

1355. Lancaster (ED's 100–148) County.

1356. Lackawanna (ED's 1–22, 32–35) County.

1357. Lackawanna (ED's 23–31, 36–49) County.

1358. Lackawanna (ED's 50–67, 137, 144, 148) County.

1359. Lackawanna (ED's 68–96, 102–104, 145, 147) County.

1360. Lackawanna (ED's 97–101, 105–136, 146) County.

1361. Lawrence (ED's 109–144) County.

1362. Lawrence (ED's 145–158) and Lebanon (ED's 135–144, 146–158) Counties.

1363. Lebanon (ED's 145, 159–172) and Lehigh (ED's 131–142, 145–150) Counties.

1364. Lehigh (ED's 143, 144, 151–177) County.

1365. Lehigh (ED's 178–210) and Luzerne (ED's 1–5) Counties.

1366. Luzerne (ED's 6–32, 172) County.

1367. Luzerne (ED's 33–52, 60–62, 171) County.

1368. Luzerne (ED's 53–59, 63–81, 86–98) County.

1369. Luzerne (ED's 82–85, 99–115, 174) County.

1370. Luzerne (ED's 116–141, 173) County.

1371. Luzerne (ED's 142–170) County.

1372. Lycoming (ED's 28–75, 104) County.

1373. Lycoming (ED's 76–103) and McKean (ED's 106–121) Counties.

1374. McKean (ED's 122–140) and Mercer (ED's 141–161, 193) Counties.

1375. Mercer (ED's 162–191) County.

1376. Mifflin, Monroe, and Montgomery (ED 65) Counties.

1377. Montgomery (ED's 62–64, 66–89, 100, 101) County.

1378. Montgomery (ED's 90–99, 102–109, 128–142) County.

1379. Montgomery (ED's 110–127, 143–157) County.

1380. Montgomery (ED's 158–165), Montour, and Northampton (ED's 54–69, 88, 89) Counties.

1381. Northampton (ED's 70–87, 90–101, 104, 105) County.

1382. Northampton (ED's 102, 103, 106–129) and Northumberland (ED's 60–63) Counties.

1383. Northumberland (ED's 53–59, 64–67, 72–89) County.

1384. Northumberland (ED's 68–71, 90–125) County.

1385. Perry and Philadelphia (ED's 1–18) Counties.

1386. Philadelphia (ED's 19–39, 79–85) County.

1387. Philadelphia (ED's 40–54, 116–130) County.

1388. Philadelphia (ED's 55–78, 131–149) County.

1389. Philadelphia (ED's 86–115, 150–158, 249–257, 1224) County.

1390. Philadelphia (ED's 159–197) County.

1391. Philadelphia (ED's 198–241, 517) County.

1392. Philadelphia (ED's 242–248, 258–290) County.

1393. Philadelphia (ED's 291–332) County.

1394. Philadelphia (ED's 333–377) County.

1395. Philadelphia (ED's 378–421) County.

1396. Philadelphia (ED's 422–463) County.

1397. Philadelphia (ED's 464–510) County.

1398. Philadelphia (ED's 511–516, 518–553) County.

1399. Philadelphia (ED's 554–567, 669–696) County.

1400. Philadelphia (ED's 568–583, 697–717) County.

1401. Philadelphia (ED's 584–626) County.

1402. Philadelphia (ED's 627–668) County.

1403. Philadelphia (ED's 718–765) County.

1404. Philadelphia (ED's 766–794, 850–862) County.

1405. Philadelphia (ED's 795–831) County.

1406. Philadelphia (ED's 832–849, 863–882) County.

1407. Philadelphia (ED's 883–925) County.

1408. Philadelphia (ED's 926–964) County.

1409. Philadelphia (ED's 965–1006) County.

1410. Philadelphia (ED's 1007–1048, 1051, 1052, 1221, 1225) County.

1411. Philadelphia (ED's 1049, 1050, 1053–1092) County.

1412. Philadelphia (ED's 1093–1140) County.

1413. Philadelphia (ED's 1141–1145, 1163–1197) County.

1414. Philadelphia (ED's 1146–1162, 1198–1220, 1222, 1223) County.

1415. Pike, Potter, and Snyder Counties.

1416. Schuylkill (ED's 1–26, 29–33) County.

1417. Schuylkill (ED's 27, 28, 34–52, 55, 56, 60, 61, 83) County.

1418. Schuylkill (ED's 53, 54, 57–59, 62–78, 94–101) County.

1419. Schuylkill (ED's 79–82, 84–93, 102–113) County.

1420. Somerset (ED's 126–162) County.

1421. Somerset (ED's 163–170), Sullivan, and Susquehanna (ED's 57–78) Counties.

1422. Susquehanna (ED's 79–89) and Tioga (ED's 133–161, 165–169) Counties.

1423. Tioga (ED's 162–164, 170, 171), Union, and Venango (ED's 104–125, 138, 139) Counties.

1424. Venango (ED's 126–137, 140–148) and Warren (ED's 149–173, 175, 176) Counties.

1425. Warren (ED's 174, 177–184) and Washington (ED's 159–182) Counties.

1426. Washington (ED's 183–220) County.

1427. Washington (ED's 221–255) County.

1428. Wayne and Westmoreland (ED's 102–115) Counties.

1429. Westmoreland (ED's 116–141) County.

1430. Westmoreland (ED's 142–155, 158, 160, 161, 170–176) County.

1431. Westmoreland (ED's 156, 157, 159, 162–169, 177–190) County.

1432. Westmoreland (ED's 191–216) County.

1433. Wyoming and York (ED's 34–66) Counties.

1434. York (ED's 67–110, 113) County.

1435. York (ED's 111, 112, 114–140) County.

RHODE ISLAND

1436. Bristol and Kent Counties.

1437. Newport and Providence (ED's 60–63, 103, 112, 113) Counties.

1438. Providence (ED's 64–87, 104, 274–277) County.

1439. Providence (ED's 88–102, 105–111, 114, 115, 294–298) County.

1440. Providence (ED's 116–120, 126–130, 141–145, 278–293) County.

1441. Providence (ED's 121–125, 131–140, 146–159) County.

1442. Providence (ED's 160–185, 272) County.

1443. Providence (ED's 186–214, 271) County.

1444. Providence (ED's 215–256) County.

1445. Providence (ED's 257–270, 273) and Washington Counties.

SOUTH CAROLINA

1446. Abbeville and Calhoun Counties.

1447. Aiken and Bamberg (ED's 25–27, 30) Counties.

1448. Bamberg (ED's 28, 29, 31–34) and Anderson (ED's 25–54, 151) Counties.

1449. Anderson (ED's 55–72) and Barnwell (ED's 35–50) Counties.

1450. Barnwell (ED's 51–57), Dorchester, and Beaufort (ED's 58–70, 74, 75) Counties.

1451. Beaufort (ED's 71–73), Marion, and Berkeley Counties.

1452. Charleston (ED's 18–53, 62–65) Counties.

1453. Charleston (ED's 54–61, 66–86) and Darlington (ED's 1–4, 6) Counties.

1454. Darlington (ED's 5, 7–15) and Cherokee Counties.

1455. Chester and Chesterfield Counties.

1456. Clarendon and Colleton (ED's 105–118) Counties.

1457. Colleton (ED's 119–127) and Florence Counties.

1458. Dillon, Georgetown, and Greenwood (ED's 73–79) Counties.

1459. Greenwood (ED's 80–99) and Edgefield Counties.

1460. Fairfield and Greenville (ED's 1–16) Counties.

1461. Greenville (ED's 17–43, 127, 128, 130) and Newberry (ED's 100–104) Counties.

1462. Newberry (ED's 105–120) and Hampton Counties.

1463. Horry and Kershaw Counties.

1464. Lancaster and Laurens (ED's 44–53, 63–66) Counties.

1465. Laurens (ED's 54–62) and Sumter Counties.

1466. Lee and Lexington (ED's 25–38, 42) Counties.

1467. Lexington (ED's 39–41), Saluda, and Marlboro (ED's 76–86) Counties.

1468. Marlboro (ED's 87–90) and York Counties.

1469. Oconee and Orangeburg (ED's 43–53, 61–63, 128, 129) Counties.

1470. Orangeburg (ED's 54–60, 64–70, 126, 130) and Pickens Counties.

1471. Richland County.

1472. Spartanburg (ED's 67–80, 87–95, 105, 106) County.

1473. Spartanburg (ED's 81–86, 96–104, 107, 108, 131) and Williamsburg (ED's 91–99) Counties.

1474. Williamsburg (ED's 100–114) and Union Counties.

SOUTH DAKOTA

1475. Armstrong, Dewey, Sterling, Washabaugh, and Bennett Counties, Wounded Knee District, and Porcupine, Washington, Shannon, Mellette, Todd, Schnasse, and Bon Homme Counties.

1476. Aurora, Beadle, Brookings, and Brule Counties.

1477. Brown, Buffalo, Butte, and Codington Counties.

1478. Campbell, Charles Mix, Clark, and Clay Counties.

1479. Corson, Custer, Davison, Day, and Deuel Counties.

1480. Douglas, Edmunds, Faulk, Fall River, and Grant Counties.

1481. Gregory, Hamlin, Hand, Hanson, and Harding Counties.

1482. Hughes, Hutchinson, Hyde, Jerauld, and Lake Counties.

1483. Kingsbury, McPherson, and Lawrence Counties.

1484. Lincoln, Marshall, Lyman, and McCook Counties.

1485. Meade, Miner, and Minnehaha (ED's 320–322, 331–347) Counties.

1486. Minnehaha (ED's 323–330, 348, 349), Moody, Pennington, and Sanborn Counties.

1487. Perkins, Tripp, Potter, and Roberts Counties.

1488. Spink, Stanley, and Sully Counties.

1489. Turner, Union, Walworth, and Yankton Counties.

TENNESSEE

1490. Anderson, Bedford, Benton, and Bledsoe Counties.

1491. Blount, Bradley, and Carroll Counties.

1492. Campbell, Cannon, and Carter Counties.

1493. Cheatham, Chester, Claiborne, Clay, and Cumberland Counties.

1494. Cocke, Coffee, Crockett, and Decatur Counties.

1495. Davidson (ED's 12–57) County.

1496. Davidson (ED's 58–98, 177) County.

1497. Davidson (ED's 99–114), De Kalb, and Dyer Counties.

1498. Dickson, Fayette, and Fentress Counties.

1499. Franklin and Gibson (ED's 33–49) Counties.

1500. Gibson (ED's 50–65), Giles, and Grundy Counties.

1501. Grainger, Greene, Hamblen, and Hamilton (ED's 84–86) Counties.

1502. Hamilton (ED's 42–59, 74–83, 87–96, 200) County.

1503. Hamilton (ED's 60–73), Hancock, and Haywood Counties.

1504. Hardeman, Hardin, and Hawkins Counties.

1505. Henderson, Henry, and Hickman Counties.

1506. Houston, Humphreys, Jackson, James, and Jefferson Counties.

1507. Johnson, Lake, and Knox (ED's 79–101, 189) Counties.

1508. Knox (ED's 102–132, 188) County.

1509. Lauderdale, Lawrence, Lewis, and Loudon Counties.

1510. Lincoln, Macon, and McMinn Counties.

1511. McNairy and Madison Counties.

1512. Marion, Marshall, Moore, and Maury (ED's 94–111) Counties.

1513. Maury (ED's 112–124, 159), Meigs, and Montgomery Counties.

1514. Monroe, Morgan, and Obion Counties.

1515. Overton, Pickett, Perry, Scott, Polk, and Sequatchie Counties.

1516. Putnam, Rhea, and Robertson Counties.

1517. Roane, Rutherford, and Trousdale Counties.

1518. Sevier and Shelby (ED's 51–79, 313, 317, 318) Counties.

1519. Shelby (ED's 80–128, 185–188, 314–316, 322, 327, 329, 330) County.

1520. Shelby (ED's 129–184, 189–223, 244–250, 324–326, 328) County.

1521. Shelby (ED's 224–243, 251–285, 320, 321, 323) and Smith Counties.

1522. Stewart, Sullivan, and Sumner (ED's 131–142) Counties.

1523. Sumner (ED's 143–148), Tipton, Unicoi, and Union Counties.

1524. Van Buren, Warren, Washington, and Wayne Counties.

1525. Weakley and Wilson Counties.

1526. White and Williamson Counties.

TEXAS

1527. Anderson, Andrews, Angelina, and Armstrong Counties.

1528. Aransas, Archer, Austin, Atascosa, Bailey, Bandera, and Bee Counties.

1529. Bastrop, Baylor, and Brazos Counties.

1530. Bell and Briscoe Counties.

1531. Bexar (ED's 1–19, 39–48, 63) County.

1532. Bexar (ED's 20–38, 49–62, 65–74, 84) County.

1533. Bexar (ED's 64, 75–83, 85–87, 219), Blanco, Borden, Brewster, Bosque, and Bowie (ED's 10–12) Counties.

1534. Bowie (ED's 1–9, 13–19), Brazoria, and Callahan Counties.

1535. Brown, Calhoun, Burleson, and Burnet (ED's 111–114, 116–118, 120, 121) Counties.

1536. Burnet (ED's 115, 119), Caldwell, and Cameron Counties.

1537. Camp, Carson, Castro, Chambers, Childress, and Cass Counties.

1538. Cherokee, Clay, Cochran, Hockley, and Coke Counties.

1539. Coleman, Crockett, Crosby, and Collin (ED's 1–16) Counties.

1540. Collin (ED's 17–30), Collingsworth, Colorado, and Comal Counties.

1541. Comanche, Concho, Dallam, and Delta Counties.

1542. Cooke, Coryell, Cottle, and Crane Counties.

1543. Dallas (ED's 19–39, 45–52, 184, 185) County.

1544. Dallas (ED's 40–44, 53–78, 101–106, 186, 187) County.

1545. Dallas (ED's 79–100, 107–109) and De Witt Counties.

1546. Dawson, Deaf Smith, Denton, Donley, and Duval Counties.

1547. Dickens, Eastland, Dimmit, Ector, Edwards, and Fannin (ED's 31–36, 39–43) Counties.

1548. Fannin (ED's 37, 38, 44–60) and El Paso (ED's 58–71, 295) Counties.

1549. El Paso (ED's 72–90, 296) and Ellis (ED's 110–122, 140–149) Counties.

1550. Ellis (ED's 123–139) and Erath (ED's 17–29, 32, 33) Counties.

1551. Erath (ED's 30, 31, 173), Falls, Floyd, and Foard Counties.

1552. Fayette, Fisher, Franklin, and Gaines Counties.

1553. Fort Bend, Frio, Freestone, and Hale Counties.

1554. Galveston and Gillespie Counties.

1555. Garza, Goliad, Gregg, Glasscock, Gray, and Grimes Counties.

1556. Gonzales and Grayson (ED's 61–74, 101–107, 142) Counties.

1557. Grayson (ED's 75–100) and Hidalgo Counties.

1558. Guadalupe, Hall, Hamilton, and Hansford Counties.

1559. Hardeman, Hardin, and Harris (ED's 46–52, 75–84, 103–108) Counties.

1560. Harris (ED's 53–74, 85–102) County.

1561. Harris (ED's 40–45, 109–121) and Harrison (ED's 33–36, 55–59) Counties.

1562. Harrison (ED's 37–54, 171), Hartley, Haskell, and Howard Counties.

1563. Hays, Hood, Hemphill, and Henderson Counties.

1564. Hill and Hopkins (ED's 59–62) Counties.

1565. Hopkins (ED's 54–58, 63–70) and Houston (ED's 59–77) Counties.

1566. Houston (ED's 78, 79), Hunt, Hutchinson, and Irion Counties.

1567. Jack, Jasper, Jackson, Karnes, King, and Kinney Counties.

1568. Jeff Davis, Jefferson, and Johnson (ED's 57–61) Counties.

1569. Johnson (ED's 41–56, 174) and Jones Counties.

1570. Kaufman, Kendall, Kent, Kerr, and Kimble Counties.

1571. Knox, Leon, La Salle, and Lamar (ED's 71–84, 96, 97) Counties.

1572. Lamar (ED's 85–95, 98–100), Lamb, Lampasas, Lee, and Lubbock Counties.

1573. Lavaca, Liberty, and Limestone (ED's 30–38) Counties.

1574. Limestone (ED's 39–49), Lipscomb, Live Oak, Llano, Winkler, Loving, Lynn, McCulloch, and Menard Counties.

1575. McLennan (ED's 74–99, 115) County.

1576. McLennan (ED's 100–111, 114), McMullen, Martin, Midland, Madison, Marion, and Mason Counties.

1577. Matagorda, Medina, Maverick, and Milam (ED's 50–59, 65–67) Counties.

1578. Milam (ED's 60–64, 68–73), Mills, Mitchell, and Polk Counties.

1579. Montague, Montgomery, Moore, and Morris Counties.

1580. Motley and Navarro Counties.

1581. Nacogdoches, Newton, Nolan, Parmer, and Pecos Counties.

1582. Nueces, Presidio, Ochiltree, Oldham, Orange, and Potter Counties.

1583. Palo Pinto, Reagan, Reeves, Roberts, Panola, and San Patricio Counties.

1584. Parker, Rains, Randall, Refugio, San Saba, and Schleicher Counties.

1585. Red River and Robertson Counties.

1586. Rockwall, Sabine, San Augustine, Runnels, and Shackelford Counties.

1587. Rusk, San Jacinto, Somervell, and Starr Counties.

1588. Scurry, Victoria, and Shelby Counties.

1589. Sherman, Smith, Stephens, and Sterling Counties.

1590. Stonewall, Sutton, and Tarrant (ED's 89–107, 118–122, 156–158) Counties.

1591. Tarrant (ED's 108–117, 123–155) County.

1592. Tarrant (ED's 159–172), Val Verde, Swisher, Throckmorton, and Tom Green Counties.

1593. Taylor, Terrell, Terry, Upton, Uvalde, and Waller Counties.

1594. Titus, Tyler, and Travis (ED's 57–65, 84–92, 138, 141) Counties.

1595. Travis (ED's 66–83, 136, 137), Trinity, and Young Counties.

1596. Upshur, Zapata, Zavalla, and Van Zandt Counties.

1597. Walker, Wichita, Wilbarger, and Williamson (ED's 115–117) Counties.

1598. Williamson (ED's 118–135, 139) and Wilson Counties.

1599. Ward, Webb, and Washington Counties.

1600. Wharton, Wheeler, and Wise Counties.

1601. Wood and Yoakum Counties.

UTAH

1602. Beaver, Box Elder, and Cache Counties.

1603. Carbon, Davis, Emery, Garfield, Grand, and Iron Counties.

1604. Juab, Kane, Millard, Morgan, Piute, Rich, San Juan, and Salt Lake (ED's 75–80) Counties.

1605. Salt Lake (ED's 81–99, 240) County.

1606. Salt Lake (ED's 100–122, 239, 241, 243) County.

1607. Salt Lake (ED's 123–145) County.

1608. Sampete, Sevier, and Summit Counties.

1609. Tooele, Uintah, and Utah (ED's 183–191) Counties.

1610. Utah (ED's 192–201), Wasatch, Washington, and Wayne Counties.

1611. Weber County.

VERMONT

1612. Addison, Bennington, and Lamoille Counties.

1613. Caledonia and Chittenden (ED's 61–74, 89–91) Counties.

1614. Chittenden (ED's 75–88), Essex, and Franklin (ED's 100–116) Counties.

1615. Franklin (ED's 117, 118), Grand Isle, Orange, and Orleans Counties.

1616. Rutland County.

1617. Washington and Windsor (ED's 267–274) Counties.

1618. Windsor (ED's 275–292, 294) and Windham Counties.

VIRGINIA

1619. Accomack and Albemarle (ED's 1–10) Counties.

1620. Albemarle (ED's 11–16) and Appamattox Counties, Alexandria (city), and Alexandria, Alleghany, and Amelia Counties.

1621. Amherst, Augusta, and Bland Counties.

1622. Bath, Bedford, and Botetourt Counties.

1623. Bristol (city), Buchanan, Brunswick, and Buckingham Counties, and Buena Vista (city).

1624. Campbell, Caroline, and Carroll Counties.

1625. Charles City and Charlotte Counties, Charlottesville (city), Clarke County, Clifton Forge (city), and Chesterfield County.

1626. Craig, Culpeper, Cumberland, and Dickenson Counties and Danville (city).

1627. Dinwiddie County, Radford (city), and Elizabeth City, Essex, and Giles Counties.

1628. Fairfax, Fauquier, Floyd, and Fluvanna Counties.

1629. Franklin and Frederick Counties, Fredericksburg (city), and Gloucester and Goochland Counties.

1630. Grayson, Greene, Greensville, and Halifax (ED's 54–65) Counties.

1631. Halifax (ED's 66–76), Hanover, and Henrico Counties.

1632. Henry, Highland, Isle of Wight, James City, King and Queen, and King George Counties and Williamsburg (city).

1633. King William, Lancaster, Lee, and Loudoun Counties.

1634. Louisa, Lunenburg, and Mathews Counties and Lynchburg (city) (ED's 77–86, 137).

1635. Lynchburg (city) (ED's 87–91, 138, 140) and Madison, Mecklenburg, and Middlesex Counties.

1636. Montgomery, Nansemond, Nelson, and New Kent Counties.

1637. Newport News (city) and Norfolk (city) (ED's 18–52).

1638. Norfolk ED's 53–70, 79, 81) and Norfolk County (ED's 71, 72, 82–85).

1639. Norfolk (ED's 73–78), Northampton, Northumberland, and Nottoway Counties.

1640. Orange, Powhatan, and Page Counties, Winchester (city), and Patrick County.

1641. Petersburg (city) and Pittsylvania (ED's 85–95, 101–115) County.

1642. Pittsylvania (ED's 96–100) County, Portsmouth (city), and Prince Edward and Prince George Counties.

1643. Prince William, Richmond, Princess Anne, Rappahannock, and Pulaski Counties.

1644. Richmond (city) (ED's 63–107).

1645. Richmond (city) (ED's 49–58, 108–145).

1646. Roanoke (city) and Roanoke County.

1647. Rockbridge and Rockingham Counties.

1648. Russell, Scott, and Shenandoah Counties.

1649. Smyth, Southampton, Spotsylvania, and Stafford Counties.

1650. Staunton (city) and Surry, Sussex, Warwick, and Tazewell Counties.

1651. Warren, Washington, Westmoreland, and York Counties.

1652. Wise and Wythe Counties.

WASHINGTON

1653. Adams, Asotin, Benton, and Chehalis (ED's 1–12, 14–26, 316, 320) Counties.

1654. Chehalis (ED's 13, 27–35), Chelan, Clallam, Ferry, and Garfield Counties.

1655. Columbia, Cowlitz, and Clark Counties.

1656. Douglas, Franklin, Grant, Island, Jefferson, and Klickitat Counties.

1657. King (ED's 7–57, 365) County.

1658. King (ED's 58–91) County.

1659. King (ED's 92–113, 146–160) County.

1660. King (ED's 114–139, 205–214, 361, 362) County.

1661. King (ED's 140–145, 161–183, 215–224) County.

1662. King (ED's 184–204, 357), Kitsap, and Kittitas (ED's 80–86) Counties.

1663. Kittitas (ED's 87–93) and Pierce (ED's 174–192, 213–230) Counties.

1664. Pierce (ED's 231–256, 269–274) County.

1665. Pierce (ED's 193–212, 257–268, 275–287, 315) County.

1666. Lewis, Lincoln, and Mason Counties.

1667. Okanogan, Pacific, San Juan, and Skagit (ED's 242–261, 358, 360, 366) Counties.

1668. Skagit (ED's 262–265, 363), Skamania, and Snohomish (ED's 266–299) Counties.

1669. Snohomish (ED's 300–315, 364) and Spokane (ED's 129–144, 207, 310, 311, 316) Counties.

1670. Spokane (ED's 145–176) County.

1671. Spokane (ED's 177–206) County.

1672. Stevens, Thurston, Wahkiakum, and Walla Walla (ED's 232–238) Counties.

1673. Walla Walla (ED's 239–256) and Whatcom (ED's 318–334) Counties.

1674. Whatcom (ED's 316, 335–356, 359) and Whitman (ED's 257–271) Counties.

1675. Whitman (ED's 272–278) and Yakima Counties.

WEST VIRGINIA

1676. Barbour, Berkeley, and Boone Counties.

1677. Braxton, Brooke, and Calhoun Counties.

1678. Cabell and Clay (ED's 1–3) Counties.

1679. Clay (ED's 4–6), Doddridge, Grant, and Fayette (ED's 7–15) Counties.

1680. Fayette (ED's 16–27), Gilmer, and Hampshire Counties.

1681. Greenbrier, Hancock, and Jackson (ED's 44–55) Counties.

1682. Jackson (ED's 56–58), Lincoln, Hardy, and Jefferson Counties.

1683. Harrison County.

1684. Kanawha (ED's 45–75) County.

1685. Kanawha (ED's 76–96 and Lewis Counties.

1686. Logan and McDowell (ED's 66–87) Counties.

1687. McDowell (ED's 88–94) and Marion Counties.

1688. Marshall and Mingo Counties.

1689. Mason and Mercer (ED's 118–135, 205) Counties.

1690. Mercer (ED's 136–144, 206), Monroe, Mineral, and Morgan Counties.

1691. Monongalia, Nicholas, and Ohio (ED's 140–143) Counties.

1692. Ohio (ED's 98–135, 144) County.

1693. Pendleton, Taylor, Pleasants, and Ritchie Counties.

1694. Pocahontas, Putnam, and Summers Counties.

1695. Preston and Raleigh Counties.

1696. Randolph, Roane, and Tucker (ED's 142, 143) Counties.

1697. Tucker (ED's 144–151) and Wood Counties.

1698. Tyler, Wyoming, Uphsur, and Webster Counties.

1699. Wayne, Wirt, and Wetzel Counties.

WISCONSIN

1700. Adams, Bayfield, Ashland, and Barron (ED's 1–4) Counties.

1701. Barron (ED's 5–25) and Brown (ED's 1–8, 25–40) Counties.

1702. Brown (ED's 9–24), Buffalo, and Burnett Counties.

1703. Calumet and Chippewa Counties.

1704. Clark and Green Counties.

1705. Columbia and Door Counties.

1706. Crawford and Dodge (ED's 1–31) Counties.

1707. Dodge (ED's 32–38) and Douglas Counties.

1708. Dane (ED's 36–78, 184) County.

1709. Dane (ED's 79–101) and Dunn Counties.

1710. Eau Claire , Forest, and Grant (ED's 14–25) Counties.

1711. Grant (ED's 26–48), Florence, and Iowa Counties.

1712. Fond du Lac County.

1713. Green Lake, Marquette, Iron, and Jackson Counties.

1714. Jefferson and Juneau Counties.

1715. Kenosha and Kewaunee Counties.

1716. La Crosse and Marinette (ED's 70–76) Counties.

1717. Marinette (ED's 77–94, 150), Lafayette, and Sawyer Counties.

1718. Langlade, Lincoln, and Manitowoc (ED's 23–32) Counties.

1719. Manitowoc (ED's 14–22, 33–42) and Marathon (ED's 70–94) Counties.

1720. Marathon (ED's 95–114) and Milwaukee (ED's 1–13, 274–276) Counties.

1721. Milwaukee (ED's 153–165, 277–296, 299) County.

1722. Milwaukee (ED's 14–28, 51–59, 178–193, 308, 311) County.

1723. Milwaukee (ED's 29–41, 74–83, 166–177, 297, 298, 305, 310) County.

1724. Milwaukee (ED's 42–50, 60–65, 84–95, 213–223, 302, 303) County.

1725. Milwaukee (ED's 66–73, 96–111, 116–123, 307) County.

1726. Milwaukee (ED's 112–115, 124–148, 300, 301) County.

1727. Milwaukee (ED's 149–152, 194–212, 224–239, 304–306) County.

1728. Milwaukee (ED's 240–273) County.

1729. Monroe and Oconto Counties.

1730. Oneida, Price, and Outagamie (ED's 116–130) Counties.

1731. Outagamie (ED's 131–149), Ozaukee, and Pepin Counties.

1732. Pierce, Rusk, and Richland Counties.

1733. Polk and Portage Counties.

1734. Racine County.

1735. Rock County.

1736. St. Croix and Sauk (ED's 104–124, 157) Counties.

1737. Sauk (ED's 125–131), Taylor, Vilas, and Shawano (ED's 139–159) Counties.

1738. Shawano (ED's 160–164), Waushara, and Sheboygan (ED's 92–107, 123–126) Counties.

1739. Sheboygan (ED's 108–122), Trempealeau, and Walworth (ED's 133, 134) Counties.

1740. Walworth (ED's 135–157) and Vernon Counties.

1741. Washburn, Waukesha, and Wood (ED's 185–189) Counties.

1742. Wood (ED's 190–207) and Washington Counties.

1743. Waupaca and Winnebago (ED's 115–127) Counties.

1744. Winnebago (ED's 128–166) County.

WYOMING

1745. Albany, Fremont, Big Horn, Carbon, and Johnson Counties.

1746. Converse, Crook, Sweetwater, and Laramie Counties.

1747. Natrona, Park, Sheridan, Uinta, and Weston Counties and Yellowstone National Park.

ALASKA

1748. First and Second (ED's 1–4) Judicial Districts.

1749. Second (ED's 5–16) and Fourth Judicial Districts.

1750. Third Judicial District.

HAWAII

1751. Hawaii (ED's 101–103, 106–113, 119–122, 125–134) County.

1752. Hawaii (ED's 96–100, 104, 105, 114–118, 123, 124), Kauai, and Kalawao Counties.

1753. Honolulu (ED's 17–35,, 50–58) County.

1754. Honolulu (ED's 36–49, 59–70, 135) County.

1755. Maui County.

PUERTO RICO

1756. Adjuntas, Culebra, Aguada, and Aguas Buenas.

1757. Aguadilla, Aibonito, and Barranquitas.

1758. Ahasco, Arroyo, and Arecibo (ED's 184–197, 209, 1054, 1055).

1759. Arecibo (ED's 198–208, 210–219), Barceloneta, and Barros (ED's 747–754).

1760. Barros (ED's 755–764) and Bayamon.

1761. Cabo Rojo and Caguas (ED's 918–930).

1762. Caguas (ED's 931–939), Camuy, Carolina, and Dorado.

1763. Cayey and Ciales.

1764. Cidra, Comerio, and Coamo.

1765. Corozal, Maricao, and Fajardo.

1766. Guayama, Guayanilla, and Gurabo.

1767. Hatillo and Humacao.

1768. Isabela and Juana Diaz (ED's 667–688).

1769. Juana Diaz (ED's 689–697), Juncos, Lajas, and Las Marias.

1770. Lares, Loiza, and Munabo.

1771. Manati and Mayaguez (ED's 425–436, 1050, 1051).

1772. Mayaguez (ED's 437–457, 1046, 1057), Moca, and Rincon.

1773. Morovis, Naranjito, Naguabo, and Patillas (ED's 783–787, 1058).

1774. Patillas (ED's 788–795), Penuelas, and Ponce (ED's 621–630).

1775. Ponce (ED's 631–666).

1776. Quebradillas, Rio Grande, and Rio Piedras.

1777. Sabana Grande, Salinas, and San German.

1778. San Juan (ED's 4–28).

1779. San Juan (ED's 1–3, 29, 30), San Lorenzo, and San Sebastian.

1780. Santa Isabel, Toa Alta, Toa Baja, Trujillo Alto, and Yabucoa.

1781. Utuado.

1782. Vega Alta, Vega Baja, Vieques, and Yauco (ED's 541–549)

1783. Yauco (ED's 550–572).

MILITARY AND NAVAL

1784. Philippines, Hospitals, Ships, and Stations.

1910 Soundex/Miracode

Index Soundex/Miracode to the 1910 Population Schedules. 4,642 rolls.

1910 census schedules have been reproduced by NARS as a separate microfilm publication for each of the 21 States.

The letter at the beginning of the Soundex code is the first letter of the surname of the individual; the number is a phonetic code for the surname, followed by the first name. A guide to the use of the Soundex system is found in appendix I of this catalog. Be sure to read the introduction carefully before ordering.

ALABAMA   T1259 (Soundex)

See rolls 119–140 for Birmingham, Mobile, and Montgomery.

1. A-000—A-330 Rebecca
2. A-330 Reese—A-450 Izah
3. A-450 J.—A-600 E.
4. A-600 E.—B-200 R.
5. B-200 S.—B-260 B.
6. B-260 C.—B-340 Z.
7. B-346—B-410 T.
8. B-410 W.—B-452 H.
9. B-452 I.—B-525 S.
10. B-525 T.—B-620 Ben P.
11. B-620 Benjamin—B-624
12. B-625—B-635 C.
13. B-635 D.—B-650 James
14. B-650 Jane—B-652 Q.
15. B-652 R.—C-100 Reuben
16. C-100 Rich—C-200 John G.
17. C-200 John H.—C-330
18. C-350—C-420
19. C-423—C-455 G.
20. C-455 H.—C-500
21. C-510—C-552 B.
22. C-552 C.—C-616 Mary
23. C-616 Mat—C-636 C.
24. C-636 D.—C-652 S.
25. C-652 T.—D-120 L.
26. D-120 M.—D-200 V.
27. D-200 W.—D-350 G.
28. D-350 H.—D-525 I.
29. D-525 J.—D-621 F.
30. D-621 G.—E-250 I.
31. E-250 J.—E-430
32. E-450—F-240 W. L.
33. F-240 Walker—F-460 Jessy
34. F-460 Jim—F-626 I.
35. F-626 J.—F-655 Wm.
36. F-655 Wm. A.—G-350 E.
37. G-350 F.—G-430
38. G-435—G-600 James
39. G-600 Jane—G-625 K.
40. G-625 L.—G-650 Marcus
41. G-650 Margaret—H-130 I.
42. H-130 J.—H-220 Theo
43. H-220 Thomas—H-300 Joel
44. H-300 John—H-400 Calton
45. H-400 Calvin—H-400 Theola
46. H-400 Thomas—H-453 Robt.
47. H-453 Rufus—H-530 U.
48. H-530 V.—H-553 O.
49. H-553 P.—H-620 Lottie
50. H-620 Lou—H-630 Joseph
51. H-630 Josephi—H-651 Jennie
52. H-651 Jesse—J-250 Classie
53. J-250 Claud—J-500 L.
54. J-500 M.—J-520 John Z.
55. J-520 Johney—J-523 F.
56. J-523 G.—J-525 Johnny
57. J-525 Johnsin—J-600
58. J-635—K-400
59. K-410—K-523 Jopper S.
60. K-523 Joseph—L-000 Herbert
61. L-000 Hester—L-200 Erein
62. L-200 Ernest—L-250 Joel
63. L-250 John—L-500 Joe
64. L-500 John—L-534 Robert
65. L-534 Roland—M-200 Darsey
66. M-200 Dave—M-230 Joshua
67. M-230 Judge—M-243 Irene
68. M-243 Isaac—M-250 Will
69. M-250 Will A.—M-261 K.
70. M-261 L.—M-324 B.
71. M-324 C.—M-421 V.
72. M-421 W.—M-500 J.
73. M-500 K.—M-600 D.
74. M-600 E.—M-620 A.
75. M-620 B.—M-626 K.
76. M-626 L.—N-200 Bell
77. N-200 Ben—N-450 K.
78. N-450 L.—O-416 Hanata
79. O-416 Hubbert—P-200 B.
80. P-200 C.—P-350 D.
81. P-350 E.—P-400 Willia
82. P-400 Wm.—P-500
83. P-510—P-620 S.
84. P-620 T.—P-630 D.
85. P-630 E.—R-000 I.
86. R-000 J.—R-162 A.
87. R-162 B.—R-200 Joel
88. R-200 John—R-262 H.
89. R-262 I.—R-326 J.
90. R-326 K.—R-520 Jap.
91. R-520 Jeff—S-150
92. S-152—S-250 Wiley
93. S-250 Will—S-320 B.
94. S-320 C.—S-351 J.
95. S-351 K.—S-364 L.
96. S-364 M.—S-435 V.
97. S-435 W.—S-520 Wilkins
98. S-520 Will—S-530 Jack S.
99. S-530 Jackius—S-530 Warsh.
100. S-530 Wash—S-542
101. S-552—S-640 V.
102. S-640 W.—T-400 C.
103. T-400 D.—T-460
104. T-500—T-520 James W.
105. T-520 Jane—T-610 A.
106. T-610 B.—T-656 Giles
107. T-656 Gim—V-525 I.
108. V-525 J.—W-250
109. W-252—W-300 Leathie
110. W-300 Lee—W-325 I.
111. W-325 J.—W-363 J.
112. W-363 K.—W-425 B.
113. W-425 C.—W-426 K.
114. W-426 L.—W-452 Dixie
115. W-452 Doc—W-452 Morton
116. W-452 Mose—W-530 E.
117. W-530 F.—W-632 Q.
118. W-632 R.—Institutions

ALABAMA CITIES: Birmingham, Mobile, and Montgomery

119. A-000—B-255
120. B-260—B-620 L.
121. B-620 M.—C-150
122. C-160—C-560
123. C-560—D-300
124. D-400—F-300
125. F-400—G-500
126. G-520—H-320
127. H-325—H-621
128. H-625—J-520
129. J-522—L-000
130. L-100—M-200
131. M-210—M-430
132. M-450—N-300
133. N-400—P-616
134. P-620—R-300
135. R-310—S-362
136. S-363—S-600
137. S-610—T-655
138. T-656—W-320
139. W-325—W-436
140. W-450—End

ARKANSAS   T1260 (Miracode)

1. A-000—A-350 Alice
2. A-350 Allen—A-450 Claud
3. A-450 Clayton—A-536 Odys
4. A-536 Ola—A-665 Sam
5. B-000—B-235 Fread
6. B-235 Genover—B-263 James
7. B-263 James—B-362 William
8. B-362 William—B-420 Lige
9. B-420 Lill—B-453 J. G.
10. B-453 J. O. MR—B-530 David B.
11. B-530 David D.—B-620 Adaville
12. B-620 Addie M.—B-623 Willie
13. B-623 Willie—B-632 Thomas E.
14. B-632 Thomas E.—B-650 David
15. B-650 David—B-650 Wesley
16. B-650 Wesley—B-653 Rufus
17. B-653 Rufus—B-666 Rosa
18. C-000—C-200 Dossie
19. C-200 Dove M.—C-260 Frank
20. C-260 Frank—C-410 Timothy
21. C-410 Tom C.—C-452 Joe
22. C-452 Joe—C-463 Willie
23. C-463 Worland—C-534 Francis
24. C-534 Frank—C-613 John F.
25. C-613 John G.—C-625 Tomun
26. C-625 Tomun—C-644 Charles H.
27. C-644 Charley—C-665 Tilda
28. D-000—D-120 Roxie
29. D-120 Roy—D-236 Willie
30. D-236 Wm.—D-355 Cora
31. D-355 Cover—D-520 James V.
32. D-520 James W.—D-616 Osie
33. D-616 Pauline—D-665 James
34. E-000—E-352 Charles P.
35. E-352 Charlie—E-516 George W.
36. E-516 H Ell—E-663 William
37. F-000—F-425 Tarrence
38. F-425 Theodore—F-534 James
39. F-534 James—F-630 Robert
40. F-630 Robert—F-666 Thomas
41. G-000—G-320 William
42. G-320 William—G-425 Luther
43. G-425 Lyngus—G-600 Antony
44. G-600 Archie—G-624 Susie
45. G-624 T. A.—G-650 Homer
46. G-650 Homer—G-666 Margaret
47. H-000—H-200 James C.
48. H-200 James E.—H-250 Cecil
49. H-250 Chaerine—H-322 Henry
50. H-322 Henry C.—H-400 Green B.
51. H-400 Green B.—H-420 Wesley
52. H-420 Wiley G.—H-500 James
53. H-500 James—H-530 Hillary W.
54. H-530 Hiram—H-546 Joseph
55. H-546 Joseph—H-620 Fellmer
56. H-620 Ferma—H-630 Elizah J.
57. H-630 Elizah J.—H-650 Lloyd C.
58. H-650 Lon—H-663 Oscar
59. I-000—I-664 John L.
60. J-000—J-250 Pealie
61. J-250 Pearl—J-520 George
62. J-520 George—J-520 T.
63. J-520 T. C.—J-525 George
64. J-525 George—J-525 Sterling
65. J-525 Sterling—J-663 James A.
66. K-000—K-460 Arthur
67. K-460 Arthur—K-534 Edward
68. K-534 Edward—K-662 Robert
69. L-000—L-200 Alvia
70. L-200 Alvia—L-240 Cain
71. L-240 Calvin—L-420 Alexander
72. L-420 Alexander—L-523 Sylvester
73. L-523 Talmage—L-665 Willie F.
74. M-000—M-200 Sallie
75. M-200 Sallie—M-235 Maggie M.
76. M-235 Magie—M-245 Thelma
77. M-245 Thoas A.—M-254 Daisy
78. M-254 Daisy—M-300 John
79. M-300 John—M-350 Jack
80. M-350 Jack—M-460 Finus
81. M-460 Firsie—M-532 Octo
82. M-532 Ora R.—M-600 Monroe
83. M-600 Monroe—M-620 William J.
84. M-620 William J.—M-635 Joe S.
85. M-635 Joe S.—M-665 George W.
86. N-000 Aen—N-400 Frank
87. N-400 Frank—N-635 Willis A.
88. N-635 Wise—N-665 Alec
89. O-000—O-520 Robert W.
90. O-520 Robt. E.—O-664 Elmer
91. P-000—P-320 James A.
92. P-320 Jimmie—P-400 Mabel A.
93. P-400 Macie—P-500 Curlie, Mrs.
94. P-500 D. A.—P-620 Florance
95. P-620 Florece—P-626 J. U.
96. P-626 J. W.—P-665 Will
97. Q-000 Abe—Q-656 Wlie
98. R-000—R-152 Susan
99. R-152 Susan E.—R-200 George
100. R-200 George—R-243 Dan
101. R-243 Frances E.—R-300 Enely
102. R-300 Enis—R-355 Wesley
103. R-355 Western V.—R-525 Gertrude
104. R-525 Gotton—R-660 John
105. S-000—S-162 Stephen E.
106. S-162 Steve—S-300 Janie
107. S-300 January—S-323 Annie
108. S-323 Annie—S-353 James M.
109. S-353 Jane—S-364 H. Mays
110. S-364 Harry—S-436 William
111. S-436 William—S-524 Alecaner

112.	S-524 Alfayete—S-530 James
113.	S-530 James—S-530 Will
114.	S-530 Will—S-552 Fred
115.	S-552 Fred—S-650 Franf T.
116.	S-650 Fred—S-665 Sudie
117.	T-000—T-400 Green
118.	T-400 Gussie—T-460 William
119.	T-460 William—T-520 Ida
120.	T-520 Ida—T-612 Willie
121.	T-612 Wm. A.—T-656 Lethis
122.	T-656 Levi—T-665 Sid
123.	U-000—U-660 Robert
124.	V-000 Alice—V-660 Nora E.
125.	W-000—W-246 William W.
126.	W-246 Willie—W-300 Jasper
127.	W-300 Jasper C.—W-325 Charlie
128.	W-325 Charlie—W-362 James
129.	W-362 James—W-420 Loa
130.	W-420 Lois—W-425 Rosa
131.	W-425 Rosa L.—W-436 George N.
132.	W-436 George T.—W-452 Harvey
133.	W-452 Harvey—W-452 William
134.	W-452 William—W-623 Charles
135.	W-623 Charles—W-656 Rufe W.
136.	W-656 Sam A.—W-665 William
137.	X-000—X-636 Bulah
138.	Y-000 Dock—Y-660 Jesse
139.	Z-000 Fred—Z-654 John

CALIFORNIA T1261 (Miracode)

1.	A-000—A-200 Joe
2.	A-200 John—A-260 Frank
3.	A-260 Frank—A-352 Samuel S.
4.	A-352 Samuel W.—A-425 Lewa
5.	A-425 Lewis—A-455 Antonio
6.	A-455 Arnold—A-536 Andrew
7.	A-536 Andrew—A-536 Mary
8.	A-536 Mary—A-626 Edward
9.	A-626 Elward Earl—A-665 Wilbur E.
10.	B-000—B-200 Henry
11.	B-200 Henry—B-230 Clara
12.	B-230 Clara—B-250 Fedde
13.	B-250 Federino—B-260 Laura L.
14.	B-260 Lawrence A.—B-320 Jonakian F.
15.	B-320 Joseph—B-356 Christian
16.	B-356 Christian—B-400 Phillip
17.	B-400 Phillip—B-422 Lizzie
18.	B-422 Lizzie J.—B-450 Jessie
19.	B-450 Jesus—B-500 Benjamin C.
20.	B-500 Benjamin H.—B-524 Valentine
21.	B-524 Wallis E.—B-535 B.
22.	B-535 Belle—B-600 George H.
23.	B-600 George H.—B-620 Caelestro
24.	B-620 Cahitola—B-620 Richard
25.	B-620 Richard—B-625 Carl
26.	B-625 Carl—B-630 Joel K.
27.	B-630 Johana—B-634 Leona
28.	B-634 Leonado—B-645 Henry
29.	B-645 Henry—B-650 James
30.	B-650 James—B-651 John
31.	B-651 John—B-653 Ernest R.
32.	B-653 Ernie—B-656 Leon
33.	B-656 Leon—B-666 James
34.	C-000—C-146 Wilbert
35.	C-146 William—C-200 Charles J.
36.	C-200 Charles J., Jr.—C-216 Henry
37.	C-216 Henry—C-245 John
38.	C-245 John—C-325 Vascra
39.	C-325 Virgil—C-400 William N.
40.	C-400 William N.—C-426 Robert S.
41.	C-426 Samuel C.—C-452 George E.
42.	C-452 George G.—C-462 Edwin
43.	C-462 Edwin—C-500 Helen M.
44.	C-500 Hellen—C-514 Frank G.
45.	C-514 Frank M.—C-520 Yow
46.	C-520 Yow—C-543 Chas.
47.	C-543 Cyrus H.—C-600 Charles L.
48.	C-600 Charles L.—C-616 Charls
49.	C-616 Chas.—C-623 Clara E.
50.	C-623 Clara E.—C-630 Peter
51.	C-630 Peter—C-640 Anna H.
52.	C-640 Anne—C-650 Charles H.
53.	C-650 Charles H.—C-656 William
54.	C-656 William—C-666 Nellie

55.	D-000—D-120 James K.
56.	D-120 James L.—D-150 Fred K. H.
57.	D-150 Freda—D-220 Fredrick
58.	D-220 G.—D-253 Eliva
59.	D-253 Ellen—D-350 Caroline
60.	D-350 Carrie—D-416 Virginia
61.	D-416 Virginia E.—D-500 Channcy T.
62.	D-500 Chard—D-520 Henry L.
63.	D-520 Henry M.—D-540 William T.
64.	D-540 William W.—D-600 James
65.	D-600 James—D-630 Mary
66.	D-630 Mary—D-666 George
67.	E-000—E-231 Manuel
68.	E-231 Maria—E-325 Thomas
69.	E-325 Thomas—E-425 Charles E.
70.	E-425 Charles Q.—E-524 Fred C.
71.	E-524 Fred D.—E-650 Lewis J.
72.	E-650 Loren—E-665 Nettie
73.	F-000—F-232 Fred L.
74.	F-232 George—F-263 John P.
75.	F-263 John S.—F-420 John W.
76.	F-420 Johnson—F-452 Howell
77.	F-452 Howell C.—F-520 Anna L.
78.	F-520 Anna M.—F-600 Jessie
79.	F-600 Jessie—F-623 Jesse B.
80.	F-623 Jesse G.—F-634 Sofa
81.	F-634 Sophei—F-652 Frank
82.	F-652 Frank—F-656 William
83.	F-656 William—F-666 Ruben
84.	G-000—G-163 Erwin W.
85.	G-163 Es K.—G-260 Emelie
86.	G-260 Emma—G-356 George W.
87.	G-356 Gracomp—G-420 Mary
88.	G-420 Mary—G-436 Angel
89.	G-436 Anna—C-514 Jane
90.	G-514 Jasper—G-550 Eugene
91.	G-550 Eugene—G-612 Wilmot
92.	G-612 Wm. H.—G-620 John
93.	G-620 John—G-630 Al
94.	G-630 Alba—G-645 Maud
95.	G-645 Maud L.—G-652 Herbert E.
96.	G-652 Herbert J.—G-666
97.	H-000—H-152 Joseph
98.	H-152 Joseph—H-200 Earl O.
99.	H-200 Earle—H-220 Annie
100.	H-220 Annie J.—H-243 Anna T.
101.	H-243 Annie—H-256 Carrie
102.	H-256 Carrie—H-320 Shirley V.
103.	H-320 Shoichi—H-400 Abell
104.	H-400 Abert—H-400 May
105.	H-400 May—H-430 Benjamin
106.	H-430 Benjamin—H-453 James S.
107.	H-453 James T.—H-516 Albert F.
108.	H-516 Albert J.—H-525 Anna
109.	H-525 Anna—H-532 Maximilian
110.	H-532 May—H-543 Samford
111.	H-543 Samuel—H-600 Irene S.
112.	H-600 Isaiah—H-620 Oscar W.
113.	H-620 Ossin R.—H-630 Helen
114.	H-630 Helen B.—H-640 Bert E.
115.	H-640 Bertha—H-655 N. R.
116.	H-655 Nasario—H-665 Suigh
117.	I-000—I-526 Cena
118.	I-526 Charles—I-664 William
119.	J-000—J-215 Louie
120.	J-215 Mary—450 Anna M.
121.	J-450 August H.—J-520 John
122.	J-520 John—J-525 Alma
123.	J-525 Alma—J-525 Ira B.
124.	J-525 Ira R.—J-525 William
125.	J-525 William—J-664 Levntine
126.	K-000—K-200 S.
127.	K-200 S.—K-300 Platt
128.	K-300 Powers—K-400 Mason
129.	K-400 Mathew—K-452 Frank
130.	K-452 Frank—K-510 Francis
131.	K-510 Francis—K-520 William
132.	K-520 William—K-534 Geo.
133.	K-534 George—K-620 H.
134.	K-620 H.—K-652 Nettie
135.	K-652 Nettie K.—K-665 Kusmo
136.	L-000—L-000 Sui Kum
137.	L-000 Suig—L-125 G.
138.	L-125 George—L-165 Teresa
139.	L-165 Teressa—L-200 Nicholas
140.	L-200 Nicholas—L-240 Josephine

141.	L-250 Julia—L-300 Frank
142.	L-300 Frank—L-362 James E.
143.	L-362 James J.—L-500 Nancy
144.	L-500 Nancy—L-520 Herman
145.	L-520 Herman—L-525 T. F.
146.	L-525 Teodore—L-550 Clark
147.	L-550 Claude—L-620 W. M.
148.	L-620 Wallace—L-666 Edward W.
149.	M-000—M-200 Helen I.
150.	M-200 Helen L.—M-214 Ruby
151.	M-215 Sarah—M-230 Manuel
152.	M-230 Manuel—M-236 Leila D.
153.	M-236 Leila J.—M-242 Rosa
154.	M-242 Rose—M-250 Charlotte M.
155.	M-250 Chas.—M-252 Frank
156.	M-252 Frank—M-255 Aloysus J.
157.	M-255 Alphonse—M-261 Clarence F.
158.	M-261 Cleveland—M-265 Willie
159.	M-265 Willie A.—M-324 Charles B.
160.	M-324 Charles B.—M-350 John M.
161.	M-350 John M.—M-420 Lizzie
162.	M-420 Lizzie A.—M-450 William W.
163.	M-450 William W.—M-460 John J.
164.	M-460 John J.—M-500 Michael
165.	M-500 Michael—M-530 Charles M.
166.	M-530 Charles V.—M-552 Nettie
167.	M-552 Nettie E.—M-600 Harry H.
168.	M-600 Harry J.—M-610 Ann
169.	M-610 Ann—M-620 Fred B.
170.	M-620 Fred B.—M-622 Victor
171.	M-622 Vinces—M-625 William H.
172.	M-625 William H.—M-635 Guadelupe
173.	M-635 Gugon—M-640 Mabel
174.	M-640 Mackie—M-660 Nellie
175.	N-000—N-213 Roy
176.	N-213 Roy W.—N-252 Emila
177.	N-252 Eva—N-400 William
178.	N-400 William—N-450 Nels
179.	N-450 Nicholas—N-620 Thomas
180.	N-620 Thomas J.—N-665 K.
181.	O-000—O-220 N.
182.	O-220 N.—O-320 Friska
183.	O-320 Genevieve—O-425 Ulrica
184.	O-425 Valentine—O-600 Margaret
185.	O-600 Margaret—O-666 Simon J.
186.	P-000—P-200 Marie
187.	P-200 Marie—P-263 Sanley I.
188.	P-263 Sarah—P-360 Mary
189.	P-360 Mary—P-362 Olil
190.	P-362 Oliva—P-412 James
191.	P-412 James—P-450 Mary A.
192.	P-450 Mary B.—P-520 M. I.
193.	P-520 Micajah—P-600 Norman
194.	P-600 N. R.—P-620 Rose
195.	P-620 Rose—P-625 William O.
196.	P-625 William P.—P-636 Frank
197.	P-636 Frank C.—P-666 Walter
198.	Q-000 Adjit Oie—Q-660 Mollie K.
199.	R-000—R-140 Parae A.
200.	R-140 Parquel—R-163 Edith
201.	R-163 Edith—R-200 Ernst
202.	R-200 Ernst S.—R-200 Pelegro
203.	R-200 Pennington—R-240 Edward J.
204.	R-240 Edward J.—R-255 John
205.	R-255 John—R-263 William
206.	R-263 William—R-320 John B.
207.	R-320 John B.—R-360 Tony
208.	R-360 Tony—R-452 Pery
209.	R-452 Pete—R-520 James J.
210.	R-520 James J.—R-543 Leslie G.
211.	R-543 Leslie S.—R-665 Mary J.
212.	S-000—S-125 Max
213.	S-125 Meron—S-152 Wilber S.
214.	S-152 Wiley T.—S-163 Minnie
215.	S-163 Minnie A.—S-223 R.
216.	S-223 Serapis—S-263 Charles J.
217.	S-263 Charley—S-312 Iddo J.
218.	S-312 Israel—S-320 M.
219.	S-320 M.—S-340 Harry
220.	S-340 Harry—S-351 Jacob
221.	S-351 Jacob—S-361 Richard
222.	S-361 Richard C.—S-363 William F.
223.	S-363 William F.—S-410 C. A.
224.	S-410 C. Albert—S-416 Antone
225.	S-416 Antone—S-432 Jay E.
226.	S-432 Jean—S-460 Melton

227.	S-460 Mexcedes C.—S-512 James W.
228.	S-512 James W.—S-520 Tisha
229.	S-520 Tom—S-530 Beatrice, Mrs.
230.	S-530 Beattie—S-530 Henry
231.	S-530 Henry—S-530 Phillip J.
232.	S-530 Phillip J.—S-535 Marion
233.	S-535 Mary—S-550 August
234.	S-550 August—S-565 S.
235.	S-565 Stanislaiss—S-620 Sarah A.
236.	S-620 Sarah A.—S-650 James W.
237.	S-650 Jeffery B.—S-666 Peter
238.	T-000—T-220 George
239.	T-220 George—T-300 Melissa C.
240.	T-300 Mellis—T-460 Anna M.
241.	T-460 Anna M.—T-512 Aerhune W.
242.	T-512 Agalea L.—T-520 Florence
243.	T-520 Florence—T-532 M.
244.	T-532 M. E.—T-616 May
245.	T-616 Meletibell—T-650 Delbert W.
246.	T-650 Della—T-666 Mary J.
247.	U-000—U-664 Otto
248.	V-000—V-410 Masuro
249.	V-410 Melva—V-525 George F.
250.	V-525 George J.—V-630 Elizabeth
251.	V-630 Enos—V-665 William H.
252.	W-000—W-200 Lisle
253.	W-200 Lizzie R.—W-250 Lonnie B.
254.	W-250 Lora—W-300 George
255.	W-300 George—W-320 James A.
256.	W-320 James B.—W-350 James
257.	W-350 James—W-400 Henry R.
258.	W-400 Henry V.—W-420 Helen
259.	W-420 Helen—W-425 Charles
260.	W-425 Charles—W-426 Andrew
261.	W-426 Andrew—W-436 Richard
262.	W-436 Richard—W-452 John W.
263.	W-452 Helen W.—W-500 You
264.	W-500 Young—W-526 Joe
265.	W-526 Joe—W-623 John
266.	W-623 John—W-650 Milton M.
267.	W-650 Minki—W-665 Willis
268.	X-000 Long Si—X-660 Marshall K.
269.	Y-000—Y-520 Alice G.
270.	Y-520 Alice I.—Y-620 Frederick
271.	Y-620 Frederick J.—Y-664 Filis
272.	Z-000 Albert—Z-663 Rosie

FLORIDA   T1262 (Miracode)

1.	A-000—A-425 Banjamin
2.	A-425 Ben—A-615 Fred
3.	A-615 H. C.—A-663 Giles
4.	B-000—B-260 Sam
5.	B-260 Sam—B-415 Josefa
6.	B-415 Joseph X.—B-525 Leon
7.	B-525 Leroy—B-623 Corneil
8.	B-623 Crawford—B-650 Cora
9.	B-650 Cora Lee—B-652 Sandy
10.	B-652 Saphotowa—B-665 William
11.	C-000—C-250 John
12.	C-250 John C.—C-452 Mary J.
13.	C-452 Mathis—C-525 Joseph
14.	C-525 Lillie—C-623 George T. B.
15.	C-623 George T. B.—C-665 Teresa
16.	D-000—D-200 Jim
17.	D-200 Jim, Jr.—D-500 Harriet M.
18.	D-500 Harry—D-655 David
19.	D-655 David—D-663 J. M.
20.	E-000—E-524 Sam
21.	E-524 Sam—E-665 Mercedes
22.	F-000—F-500 F. H.
23.	F-500 Foedine E.—F-655 Juan
24.	F-655 Juan F.—F-665 Willis
25.	G-000—G-420 John T.
26.	G-420 John W.—G-613 Lizzie
27.	G-613 Lothie—G-650 John
28.	G-650 John—G-666 M. R.
29.	H-000—H-252 Henry
30.	H-252 Henry B.—H-400 John A.
31.	H-400 John A.—H-520 Mac
32.	H-520 Mace—H-614 Clispern
33.	H-614 Ener J.—H-635 William
34.	H-635 William—H-665 William
35.	I-000—I-655 Lillis
36.	J-000—J-520 David
37.	J-520 David—J-525 Bethena
38.	J-525 Betsi—J-525 Walton W.

39.	J-525 Wanita—J-663 Wesley
40.	K-000—K-530 Frederick
41.	K-530 G. W.—K-666 Olof
42.	L-000—L-200 William
43.	L-200 William—L-520 Mamie
44.	L-520 Mamie—L-665 Wm.
45.	M-000—M-236 Alex
46.	M-236 Alfred—M-252 Eullia
47.	M-252 Everitt—M-324 C. B.
48.	M-324 C. Ray—M-460 Sim
49.	M-460 Simon—M-600 Peter
50.	M-600 Peter—M-635 L. Bradford
51.	M-635 L. C.—M-663 John E.
52.	N-000—N-652 Peter
53.	N-652 Reta—N-663 Tena
54.	0-000—0-662 Richard
55.	P-000—P-365 Padro
56.	P-365 Pepe—P-600 Hanna Harris
57.	P-600 Hannah—P-636 Joe
58.	P-636 Joe, Jr.—P-665 Thos. D.
59.	Q-000 Gustavus—Q-652 John
60.	R-000—R-163 Jim
61.	R-163 Jim—R-260 William
62.	R-260 William—R-400 Sam
63.	R-400 Samuel—R-663 Roman P.
64.	S-000—S-260 Frank
65.	S-260 Frank L.—S-351 Richard
66.	S-351 Rosa—S-435 Clara
67.	S-435 Cornelia—S-530 Eddie
68.	S-530 Eddie—S-536 James
69.	S-536 James—S-642 Georgia Alberd
70.	S-642 Hama—S-665 S.
71.	T-000—T-512 David
72.	T-512 David S.—T-600 Andrew
73.	T-600 Anna B.—T-664 Henretta
74.	U-000—U-655 Walter
75.	V-100 Helen—V-665 Irene
76.	W-000—W-300 Lee
77.	W-300 Lee—W-365 A. V.
78.	W-365 Aanan—W-426 Emma V.
79.	W-426 Emmett—W-452 Frank
80.	W-452 Frank—W-453 Frank M.
81.	W-453 Fred—W-660 Will
82.	X-200 Marion—X-616 C. E.
83.	Y-000 Bearter L.—Y-656 William
84.	Z-000 Adrian—Z-656 Jesse

GEORGIA   T1263 (Soundex)
See rolls 149–174 for Atlanta, Augusta, Macon, and Savannah.

1.	A-000—A-325 J.
2.	A-325 K.—A-423
3.	A-425—A-520 K.
4.	A-520 L.—A-620
5.	A-621—B-200 I.
6.	B-200 J.—B-250 E.
7.	B-250 F.—B-300 M.
8.	B-300 N.—B-362 J.
9.	B-362 K.—B-400 Wm. H.
10.	B-400 Wm. J.—B-435 R.
11.	B-435 S.—B-516
12.	B-520—B-535 K.
13.	B-535 L.—B-620 D.
14.	B-620 E.—B-623 V.
15.	B-623 W.—B-631 R.
16.	B-631 Sallie—B-650 Acie
17.	B-650 Ada—B-650 Jodis J.
18.	B-650 Joe—B-650 William
19.	B-650 Wm.—B-653 Hazel
20.	B-653 Helan—C-100 F.
21.	C-100 G.—C-160 Z.
22.	C-162—C-235 L.
23.	C-235 M.—C-400 Clint
24.	C-400 Clyde—C-432 Jessie
25.	C-432 Jim—C-455 E.
26.	C-455 F.—C-462 Thos.
27.	C-462 Thos. B.—C-520 G.
28.	C-520 H.—C-600 B.
29.	C-600 C.—C-620 J.
30.	C-620 K.—C-636 Ella M.
31.	C-636 Ellen—C-652 E.
32.	C-652 F.—D-120 I.
33.	D-120 J.—D-130 S.
34.	D-130 T.—D-250 B.
35.	D-250 C.—D-400 B.
36.	D-400 C.—D-520 K.

37.	D-520 L.—D-542 I.
38.	D-542 J.—D-650 Joe T.
39.	D-650 John—E-236 D.
40.	E-236 E.—E-420 G.
41.	E-420 H.—F-000 L.
42.	F-000 M.—F-430 I.
43.	F-430 J.—F-460 O.
44.	F-460 P.—F-626 B.
45.	F-626 C.—F-655 I.
46.	F-655 J.—G-200 S.
47.	G-200 T.—G-416 B.
48.	G-416 C.—G-454 J.
49.	G-455—G-612 N.
50.	G-612 O.—G-625 S.
51.	G-625 T.—G-650 G.
52.	G-650 H.—G-653 R.
53.	G-653 S.—H-200 Allan
54.	H-200 Allen—H-230 I.
55.	H-230 J.—H-253 F.
56.	H-263—H-325 S.
57.	H-325 T.—H-400 James
58.	H-400 Jas. A.—H-410 R.
59.	H-410 S.—H-453 J.
60.	H-453 K.—H-522 Jim
61.	H-522 Joe—H-536 M.
62.	H-536 N.—H-610 V.
63.	H-610 W.—H-620 Mallie
64.	H-620 Mamie—H-630 G.
65.	H-630 H.—H-635 Wm.
66.	H-635 Wm. A.—I-500 G.
67.	I-500 H.—J-250 F.
68.	J-250 G.—J-300 L.
69.	J-300 M.—J-520 Henry
70.	J-520 Henry A.—J-520 Robt.
71.	J-520 Robt. A.—J-525 Claus
72.	J-525 Clay—J-525 Laucer
73.	J-525 Laura—J-525 Wm. W.
74.	J-525 Wm. Y.—K-200
75.	K-246—K-510 J.
76.	K-510 K.—K-523 S.
77.	K-523 T.—L-000 H.
78.	L-000 I.—L-160
79.	L-200—L-231 D.
80.	L-231 E.—L-340 Ora
81.	L-340 Osca—L-520 E.
82.	L-520 F.—L-560 B.
83.	L-560 C.—M-142
84.	M-200—M-210
85.	M-215—M-240 Jake
86.	M-240 Jas.—M-246 G.
87.	M-246 H.—M-254 N.
88.	M-254 O.—M-300 F.
89.	M-300 G.—M-324 D.
90.	M-324 E.—M-420 M.
91.	M-420 N.—M-460 Samson S.
92.	M-460 Samual W.—M-540 J.
93.	M-540 K.—M-600 P.
94.	M-600 Q.—M-620 W.
95.	M-620 XYZ—M-635 E.
96.	M-635 F.—N-200 Joe
97.	N-200 Joe A.—N-425 F.
98.	N-425 G.—O-242 K.
99.	O-242 L.—O-610
100.	P-000—P-250
101.	P-260—P-362 Lea
102.	P-362 Lee—P-412 Lou
103.	P-412 Louesa—P-525 D.
104.	P-525 E.—P-620 John
105.	P-620 John A.—P-626 C.
106.	P-626 D.—P-652 G.
107.	P-652 H.—R-152 Angie
108.	R-152 Ann—R-163 Elec
109.	R-163 Eli—R-200 J.
110.	R-200 K.—R-260 G.
111.	R-260 D.—R-300 J.
112.	R-300 K.—R-400 C.
113.	R-400 D.—R-534 C.
114.	R-534 D.—S-130 R.
115.	S-130 S.—S-165 J.
116.	S-165 K.—S-300 Willie
117.	S-300 Willie—S-323
118.	S-326—S-354 H.
119.	S-354 I.—S-363 Mary
120.	S-363 Mat—S-432
121.	S-435—S-520 B.
122.	S-520 C.—S-530 Charley
123.	S-530 Charlie—S-530 Joe

124.	S-530 Joel—S-530 Silvey	31.	B-420 Rich—B-426 Chasm	118.	E-256 Frank—E-350 Roeekah
125.	S-530 Sim—S-542 L.	32.	B-426 Chas. R.—B-436 John	119.	E-350 Rosalind S.—E-416 Elbert
126.	S-542 M.—S-616 L.	33.	B-436 John—B-452 John	120.	E-416 Elizabeth—E-430 Mary E.
127.	S-616 M.—T-240	34.	B-452 John—B-460 Rebina	121.	E-430 Mary E.—E-520 John
128.	T-250—T-455 Q.	35.	B-460 Reed—B-500 Peter	122.	E-520 John—E-550 John N.
129.	T-455 R.—T-512 E.	36.	B-500 Peter—B-520 Tillie	123.	E-550 John S.—E-625' John
130.	T-512 F.—T-520 Jenks	37.	B-520 Tillie—B-526 John	124.	E-625 John—E-665 Victor
131.	T-520 Jennie—T-560 E.	38.	B-526 John—B-534 Bertha	125.	F-000—F-200 Lozzie
132.	T-560 F.—T-650	39.	B-534 Bertha M.—B-550 William	126.	F-200 Lucey—F-236 Sarah C.
133.	T-653—U-500 Jim M.	40.	B-550 William—B-600 Gelbert E.	127.	F-236 Sarah Erola—F-260 Lena
134.	U-500 Joe—W-100	41.	B-600 Geneva—B-610 David	128.	F-260 Lena—F-326 Helen
135.	W-120—W-252 Cilla	42.	B-610 David—B-620 Charles O.	129.	F-326 Helen—F-416 Michael
136.	W-252 Cinda—W-300 John D.	43.	B-620 Charles O.—B-620 John	130.	F-416 Michael J.—F-430 Cyrus
137.	W-300 John E.—W-324	44.	B-620 John C.—B-620 Tom	131.	F-430 Cyrus—F-450 Harry A.
138.	W-325—W-350 I.	45.	B-620 Tom—B-623 Glenn	132.	F-450 Harry L.—F-460 Elizabeth
139.	W-350 J.—W-420 Charity	46.	B-623 Glenn—B-625 Emil	133.	F-460 Elizabeth—F-520 George
140.	W-420 Charles—W-425 Emily	47.	B-625 Emil—B-626 H. P.	134.	F-520 George—F-552 John A.
141.	W-425 Emma—W-426 James	48.	B-626 H. R.—B-630 Henry	135.	F-552 John A.—F-620 Adaline
142.	W-426 James A.—W-446	49.	B-630 Henry—B-632 Clifford	136.	F-620 Adam—F-623 Edgar
143.	W-450—W-452 Govan	50.	B-632 Clinton M.—B-634 John	137.	F-623 Edith—F-630 George W.
144.	W-452 Grace—W-452 Myrtle	51.	B-634 John—B-635 Ursula E.	138.	F-630 George W.—F-636 Agnes
145.	W-452 N.—W-500 Kern	52.	B-635 Vada—B-650 Alex	139.	F-636 Agnes—F-650 John A.
146.	W-500 L.—W-623 McKinley	53.	B-650 Alex—B-650 George	140.	F-650 John B.—F-652 Mabel
147.	W-623 M.—W-651 I.	54.	B-650 George—B-650 Maggie	141.	F-652 Mabel—F-655 Rupert W.
148.	W-651 P.—End @010GEORGIA	55.	B-650 Maggie—B-650 William J.	142.	F-655 Russel M.—F-666 Zula
	CITIES: Atlanta, Augusta, Macon,	56.	B-650 William, Jr.—B-652 James	143.	G-000—G-150 Agnes
	Savannah	57.	B-652 James—B-653 Arthur G.	144.	G-150 Alace— G-200 Martin
149.	A-000—B-210	58.	B-653 Artie—B-653 William H.	145.	G-200 Martin—G-240 Joseph
150.	B-230—B-500	59.	B-653 William I.—B-656 Emma	146.	G-240 Joseph—G-300 William
151.	B-510—B-650 G.	60.	B-656 Emma E.—B-666 Susan A.	147.	G-300 William—G-350 Clark
152.	B-650 H.—C-300	61.	C-000—C-142 Richard B.	148.	G-350 Claude—G-400 F. Nurtine
153.	C-310—C-610	62.	C-142 Rosie— C-160 Joe	149.	G-400 F. O.—G-420 Andrew
154.	C-614—D-252	63.	C-160 Joe—C-200 Fred	150.	G-420 Andrew—G-425 Sam
155.	D-260—E-421	64.	C-200 Fred B.—C-200 Stennie	151.	G-425 Sam—G-432 Rina E.
156.	E-430—F-656	65.	C-200 Stephen—C-235 George	152.	G-432 Robert—G-455 Fancy
157.	G-000—G-635	66.	C-235 George—C-255 Charles	153.	G-455 Fannie—G-520 Gerge
158.	G-636—H-326	67.	C-255 Charles—C-325 Frances	154.	G-520 Gerge—G-542 Josephine
159.	H-350—H-600	68.	C-325 Francis—C-400 Francis	155.	G-542 Josephine—G-600 Sanford
160.	H-616—J-250	69.	C-400 Francis—C-414 Thomas H.	156.	G-600 Sarah—G-613 Johanna
161.	J-300—J-600	70.	C-414 Thos. J.—C-425 Agnes W.	157.	G-613 John—G-620 Calvin M.
162.	J-635—L-200	71.	C-425 Alaf—C-436 Edward	158.	G-620 Camillo—G-621 Jim
163.	L-210—M-230	72.	C-436 Edward—C-452 Frank	159.	G-621 Jim C.—G-626 Charlie
164.	M-235—M-451	73.	C-452 Frank—C-455 Renold	160.	G-626 Charlotte-G-632 William
165.	M-460—M-650	74.	C-455 Reyra E.—C-462 Howard	161.	G-632 William—G-642 Emil H.
166.	N-000—P-411	75.	C-462 Howard—C-500 Edgar	162.	G-642 Emma—G-650 Joseph
167.	P-412—R-162	76.	C-500 Edith—C-512 Anterius	163.	G-650 Joseph—G-652 Jacob
168.	R-163—R-566	77.	C-512 Anthony—C-516 Bruce	164.	G-652 Jacob—G-655 Emily
169.	R-600—S-364	78.	C-516 Burditt—C-530 Alice	165.	G-655 Emily—G-666 Robert
170.	S-365—S-536	79.	C-530 Alice—C-540 Shenwan	166.	H-000—H-122 Katherine
171.	S-540—T-520	80.	C-540 Sherman—C-560 Benj.	167.	H-122 Lela—H-155 August W.
172.	T-521—W-300	81.	C-560 Benj.—C-600 Etta	168.	H-155 August W.—H-160 John W.
173.	W-310—W-451	82.	C-600 Etta—C-613 Sarah	169.	H-160 John W.—H-200 Charles
174.	W-452—End	83.	C-613 Sarah J.—C-620 Edgar	170.	H-200 Charles—H-200 John
		84.	C-620 Edgar M.—C-623 Belle	171.	H-200 John—H-200 Wm.

ILLINOIS   T1264 (Miracode)

1.	A-000—A-165 Gust	85.	C-623 Belle—C-625 Frank	172.	H-200 Wm.—H-230 William
2.	A-165 Gustaf—A-240 James H.	86.	C-625 Frank—C-632 Marjorie M.	173.	H-230 Willie—H-243 Harry
3.	A-240 James M.—A-322 Sara	87.	C-632 Mark D.—C-640 Agnes M.	174.	H-243 Hattie—H-251 Nancy J.
4.	A-322 Sara—A-352 John	88.	C-640 Agnes M.—C-642 Carl V.	175.	H-251 Nathan—H-255 Mary
5.	A-352 John—A-416 Guisppe	89.	C-642 Carl Victor—C-645 Enerst	176.	H-255 Mary—H-300 Elijah
6.	A-416 Gunnai—A-426 Wilhelmin	90.	C-645 Enrico—C-652 Goldie	177.	H-300 Elijah W.—H-320 William
7.	A-426 Wilhelmina—A-450 Minnice A.	91.	C-652 Gottlieb—C-660 Sidney A.	178.	H-320 William—H-340 Mary F.
8.	A-450 Minnie—A-524 Arnette	92.	C-660 Sophia H.—C-666 Wamick L.	179.	H-340 Mary L.—H-400 Al J.
9.	A-524 Arthur—A-536 Anna	93.	D-000—D-120 Bella	180.	H-400 Alba—H-400 Herber
10.	A-536 Anna—A-536 Frances C.	94.	D-120 Bella—D-120 Martin	181.	H-400 Herbert—H-400 Samuel
11.	A-536 Frances C.—A-536 Lewis	95.	D-120 Martin—D-132 John	182.	H-400 Samuel—H-420 Grigor
12.	A-536 Lewis—A-540 Nis	96.	D-132 John—D-160 Koneganda	183.	H-420 Gus—H-430 James B.
13.	A-540 Nis—A-636 Louis C.	97.	D-160 Ladislav—D-200 Samuel	184.	H-430 James F.—H-450 John
14.	A-636 Louisa J.—A-654 J. H.	98.	D-200 Samuel—D-242 Michael	185.	H-450 John—H-455 Albertina
15.	A-654 J. M.—A-665 Wilhelmine	99.	D-242 Michael—D-252 Joseph	186.	H-455 Albertina L.—H-500 Guy
16.	B-000—B-160 William	100.	D-252 Joseph—D-265 Mary	187.	H-500 Guy—H-516 Mattie
17.	B-160 William—B-200 Henry	101.	D-265 Mary—D-340 Rysdon	188.	H-516 Maude—H-520 Sylvia
18.	B-200 Henry—B-200 William	102.	D-340 Salvatore—D-400 Henry	189.	H-520 T. Lepphelia—H-525 Florence
19.	B-200 William—B-230 Ezra	103.	D-400 Henry—D-420 Dommick	190.	H-525 Florence E.—H-530 George
20.	B-230 F. C.—B-240 Frederick	104.	D-420 Domnic—D-450 Richard	191.	H-530 George—H-536 Frank
21.	B-240 Frederick—B-250 Mary	105.	D-450 Richard—D-500 George	192.	H-536 Frank—H-543 F. Franklin
22.	B-250 Mary—B-260 Albert	106.	D-500 George—D-513 Eddie	193.	H-543 F. J.—H-553 Guy
23.	B-260 Albert—B-260 Mark	107.	D-513 Edward H.—D-522 August	194.	H-553 Hannah—H-565 Antone
24.	B-260 Mark—B-300 Ernest E.	108.	D-522 Boeris—D-535 Philip	195.	H-565 Arora E.—H-616 James
25.	B-300 Ernest E.—B-320 Michael	109.	D-535 Phoror I.—D-550 James	196.	H-616 James—H-620 N. L.
26.	B-320 Michak—B-346 John	110.	D-550 James—D-600 Fred	197.	H-620 N. R.—H-625 Martin
27.	B-346 John—B-363 Frank A.	111.	D-600 Fred—D-620 Grant	198.	H-625 Martin P.—H-630 Leola C.
28.	B-363 Franklin—B-400 John A. W.	112.	D-620 Gretia—D-626 William	199.	H-630 Leon—H-635 Benjamin B.
29.	B-400 John Allan—B-420 August	113.	D-626 William—D-652 Paul	200.	H-635 Bennatt—H-642 Leve C.
30.	B-420 August—B-420 Rich	114.	D-652 Paul—D-666 John P.	201.	H-642 Lloyd—H-652 Mary
		115.	E-000—E-162 Gerhard	202.	H-652 Mary—H-666 Edward
		116.	E-162 Gerit—E-235 Presley W.	203.	I-000—I-520 Russell
		117.	E-235 Raymond—E-256 Florence	204.	I-520 Ruth—I-665 William

205.	J-000—J-210 Maria	
206.	J-210 Maria—J-232 Joseph	
207.	J-232 Joseph—J-252 Augusta	
208.	J-252 Austave—J-500 Japp	
209.	J-500 Jas.—J-520 Frank	
210.	J-520 Frank—J-520 Michele	
211.	J-520 Micky—J-523 John M.	
212.	J-523 John D.—J-525 Birger	
213.	J-525 Bivian—J-525 Emily	
214.	J-525 Emily—J-525 Ida	
215.	J-525 Ida—J-525 Louise E.	
216.	J-525 Louise J.—J-525 Samuel	
217.	J-525 Samuel—J-552 Richard	
218.	J-552 Richard—J-640 Max	
219.	J-640 Minnie—J-665 Samuel	
220.	K-000—K-140 Fred, Sr.	
221.	K-140 Frederika—K-163 Henry	
222.	K-163 Herbert—K-212 Joseph	
223.	K-212 Joseph—K-240 Fred	
224.	K-240 Fred—K-256 John	
225.	K-256 John—K-320 Mike	
226.	K-320 Mike—K-400 Benj.	
227.	K-400 Benj.—K-400 Patrick	
228.	K-400 Patrick—K-420 George	
229.	K-420 George—K-432 John	
230.	K-432 John—K-452 George	
231.	K-452 George—K-460 Mary	
232.	K-460 Mary—K-500 Peter	
233.	K-500 Peter—K-516 Peter	
234.	K-516 Peter—K-520 Mike	
235.	K-520 Mike—K-525 Grover N.C.	
236.	K-525 Grover W.—K-532 Halvoe	
237.	K-532 Hanley—K-552 Alexander	
238.	K-552 Alexander—K-612 Albert	
239.	K-612 Albert—K-620 John F.	
240.	K-620 John F.—K-624 Joseph	
241.	K-624 Joseph—K-632 Herman H.	
242.	K-632 Herman O.—K-650 Tilie	
243.	K-650 Timothy—K-662 William	
244.	K-663 Edward—K-666 Mauas	
245.	L-000—L-100 Carrie	
246.	L-100 Carrie—L-130 Abraham	
247.	L-130 Abraham—L-152 E. L.	
248.	L-152 E. W.—L-200 Adam	
249.	L-200 Adam—L-200 James	
250.	L-200 James—L-200 William	
251.	L-200 William—L-230 Walter	
252.	L-230 Walter D.—L-250 James	
253.	L-250 James—L-260 William	
254.	L-260 William—L-320 Herman	
255.	L-320 Herman—L-350 Mary	
256.	L-350 Mary—L-426 Charlie	
257.	L-426 Christine—L-500 Suseanna	
258.	L-500 Susie—L-520 Charles	
259.	L-520 Charles—L-520 Martha N.	
260.	L-520 Marthew—L-524 Christ	
261.	L-524 Christen—L-531 Per O.	
262.	L-531 Perry—L-535 Elsie	
263.	R-535 Elsie—R-550 Walter	
264.	L-550 Walter—L-600 John W.	
265.	L-600 John W.—L-625 Jens	
266.	L-625 Jens—L-652 John	
267.	L-652 John—L-665 Victro	
268.	M-000—M-200 Albert	
269.	M-200 Albert—M-200 John	
270.	M-200 John—M-210 Dudley	
271.	M-210 E. E.—M-216 Praxeda	
272.	M-216 R. H.—M-230 Isaac	
273.	M-230 Isaac B.—M-235 Leslie	
274.	M-235 Lesly—M-240 J. M.	
275.	M-240 J. P.—M-242 Ignatz	
276.	M-242 Ignatz—M-245 George	
277.	M-245 George—M-250 Chester	
278.	M-250 Chester—M-250 Thomas	
279.	M-250 Thomas—M-252 Wm. F.	
280.	M-252 Wm. F.—M-254 William	
281.	M-254 William—M-260 Annie	
282.	M-260 Annie—M-262 Andrew	
283.	M-262 Andrew—M-263 Thomas	
284.	M-263 Thomas—M-300 Mel	
285.	M-300 Melisa—M-320 W.	
286.	M-320 W. A.—M-325 Emil P.	
287.	M-325 Emil P.—M-352 Charles	
288.	M-352 Charles—M-412 Luigi	
289.	M-412 Marcyana—M-422 Antonio	
290.	M-422 August—M-450 August	
291.	M-450 August—M-455 John	
292.	M-455 John—M-460 Ernest	
293.	M-460 Ernest—M-460 John	
294.	M-460 John—M-460 Thedore	
295.	M-460 Thees F.—M-500 Louis	
296.	M-500 Louis—M-521 Catherine	
297.	M-521 Catherine—M-532 Daniel	
298.	M-532 Daniel—M-550 Saml	
299.	M-550 Samuel—M-600 C. E.	
300.	M-600 C. F.—M-600 Herbert	
301.	M-600 Herbert—M-600 Murel	
302.	M-600 Murfin—M-610 Ignatius	
303.	M-610 Ignatius N.—M-620 Barnett	
304.	M-620 Barney—M-620 John	
305.	M-620 John—M-620 William	
306.	M-620 William—M-624 Simon	
307.	M-624 Simon—M-626 Anton	
308.	M-626 Anton—M-635 Cathrien I.	
309.	M-635 Cathryn—M-635 Ora	
310.	M-635 Ora—M-650 J. M.	
311.	M-650 J. Mrs.—M-665 Vincrzo	
312.	N-000—N-153 Reka	
313.	N-153 Sarah—N-220 John	
314.	N-220 John—N-242 S. D.	
315.	N-242 S. F.—N-325 Ida	
316.	N-325 Isaac—N-340 Samuel	
317.	N-400 Samuel—N-425 Gustav	
318.	N-425 Gustav—N-435 Christina	
319.	N-435 Clinton—N-550 Earl	
320.	N-550 Earnest C.—N-622 Antonas	
321.	N-622 Antone—N-666 Agusta	
322.	O-000—O-165 Mattie	
323.	O-165 Maud—O-236 Herma	
324.	O-236 Herman—O-260 Andrew	
325.	O-260 Andrew—O-400 Earnest	
326.	O-400 Earnest—O-425 John	
327.	O-425 John—O-465 Mary	
328.	O-465 Mary—O-560 Fraces	
329.	O-560 Francis—O-665 Winnie	
330.	P-000—P-160 Awhose J.	
331.	P-160 Barbara—P-200 Mathias	
332.	P-200 Matilda—P-236 Henry	
333.	P-236 Henry—P-265 Joe	
334.	P-265 John—P-326 Arthur	
335.	P-326 Arthur D.—P-360 Mary	
336.	P-360 Mary—P-362 Enich R.	
337.	P-362 Enllie—P-362 Marion	
338.	P-362 Marion—P-400 Charley	
339.	P-400 Charley—P-412 Elmer	
340.	P-412 Elmer—P-420 Marie	
341.	P-420 Marie—P-435 Joe	
342.	P-435 Joe—P-456 Lottie L.	
343.	P-456 Louis—P-520 Theodore	
344.	P-520 Theresa—P-560 Louise	
345.	P-560 Luther E.—P-620 Alma	
346.	P-620 Alma—P-620 Lucuis W.	
347.	P-620 Lucy—P-623 Rosey	
348.	P-623 Rosie—P-625 Otis	
349.	P-625 Ottis—P-630 Lillian	
350.	P-630 Lillian—P-640 Dacid	
351.	P-640 Daniel—P-660 Charles	
352.	P-660 Charles—P-666 Phillip	
353.	Q-000—Q-655 Andrew	
354.	R-000—R-100 Maud	
355.	R-100 Maud E.—R-143 Lawrence	
356.	R-143 Lewis—R-152 William	
357.	R-152 William—R-163 Louis	
358.	R-163 Louis—R-200 Dorothy A.	
359.	R-200 Dorothy L.—R-200 John	
360.	R-200 John—R-200 Susian	
361.	R-200 Susie—R-230 Charley	
362.	R-230 Charley H.—R-240 Kathern	
363.	R-240 Kathern C.—R-251 Edward	
364.	R-251 Edward—R-256 John	
365.	R-256 John—R-263 Cornelia S.	
366.	R-263 Cornelius—R-300 Doris L.	
367.	R-300 Dorman—R-300 Stuart	
368.	R-300 Stuart—R-320 W.	
369.	R-320 W.—R-343 C. H.	
370.	R-343 C. N.—R-360 John	
371.	R-360 John—R-400 Sadie	
372.	R-400 Sadie L.—R-500 Calix	
373.	R-500 Calow—R-500 Tom	
374.	R-500 Tom—R-521 Frank	
375.	R-521 Frank—R-534 Tommie	
376.	R-534 Ttony—R-553 Ea	
377.	R-553 Earl—R-663 Pete	
378.	S-000—S-100 John D.	
379.	S-100 John D.—S-124 S. M.	
380.	S-124 S. W.—S-142 Joseph	
381.	S-142 Joseph—S-152 Kazmir	
382.	S-152 Kazmur—S-160 Ignac	
383.	S-160 Ignacio—S-162 Mina	
384.	S-162 Mina—S-165 Ernest	
385.	S-165 Ernest A.—S-200 Mary E.	
386.	S-200 Mary E.—S-236 Charlotta	
387.	S-236 Charlotte M.—S-252 Louise	
388.	S-252 Maggie—S-300 Clifford L.	
389.	S-300 Cloid—S-300 William	
390.	S-300 William—S-315 Elbert	
391.	S-315 Elberty—S-316 Martin A.	
392.	S-316 Martin D.—S-321 Edward	
393.	S-321 Elia—S-326 Henry	
394.	S-326 Henry—S-340 Elizabeth	
395.	S-340 Elizabeth—S-345 George	
396.	S-345 George—S-350 Rebecca	
397.	S-350 Rebecca—S-352 Louis	
398.	S-352 Louis—S-356 William	
399.	S-356 William—S-362 Claude	
400.	S-362 Clay—S-363 David	
401.	S-363 David—S-364 Marvin	
402.	S-364 Marvin—S-400 Alex	
403.	S-400 Alex—S-412 Dominic	
404.	S-412 Dorothy—S-416 James G.	
405.	S-416 James H.—S-423 Gust A., Jr.	
406.	S-423 Gustave—S-432 Geodst	
407.	S-432 Georg—S-436 William S.	
408.	S-436 William V.—S-455 Sarah	
409.	S-455 Sarah—S-500 Henry	
410.	S-500 Henry—S-512 Laura	
411.	S-512 Laura M.—S-520 Hemry	
412.	S-520 Hemry—S-524 Mary	
413.	S-524 Mary—S-526 Anna	
414.	S-526 Anna—S-530 Camiel	
415.	S-530 Campbell—S-530 Francis	
416.	S-530 Francis—S-530 Jake	
417.	S-530 Jake—S-530 Lucy	
418.	S-530 Lucy—S-530 Sarah	
419.	S-530 Sarah—S-532 Halleck B.	
420.	S-532 Hampton—S-536 Edward	
421.	S-536 Edward—S-536 Wiley H.	
422.	S-536 Wiley W.—S-550 Albert	
423.	S-550 Albert—S-552 William	
424.	S-552 William—S-563 Henry	
425.	S-563 Henry—S-610 Mary	
426.	S-610 Mary—S-620 Lucy H.	
427.	S-620 Lucy R.—S-630 William	
428.	S-630 William—S-636 Otto	
429.	S-636 Otto—S-654	
430.	S-655—S-666 William	
431.	T-000—T-163 William	
432.	T-163 William—T-251 Anna	
433.	T-251 B. W.—T-320 George C.	
434.	T-320 George E.—T-414 Henry	
435.	T-414 John—T-460 Elsie	
436.	T-460 Elsie—T-500 Frank	
437.	T-500 Frank—T-512 Lewis	
438.	T-512 Lewis—T-520 Geo. W.	
439.	T-520 George—T-525 Chas.	
440.	T-525 Chester—T-562 Sara	
441.	T-562 Stanley—T-616 Clarence S.	
442.	T-616 Class—T-625 Oscar	
443.	T-625 Oscar—T-650 Sam	
444.	T-650 Sam—T-656 Hershell	
445.	T-656 Hester—T-665 William	
446.	U-000—U-536 Charles	
447.	U-536 Charles—U-665 Claus	
448.	V-000—V-240 Mary	
449.	V-240 Mary—V-400 Fred C.	
450.	V-400 Fred G.—V-500 William	
451.	V-500 William—V-526 Maurine	
452.	V-526 Max—V-561 Hess	
453.	V-561 Hess—V-666 Oscar	
454.	W-000—W-160 Grover C.	
455.	W-160 Grover O.—W-200 Louis	
456.	W-200 Louis—W-230 Mary	
457.	W-230 Mary—W-242 Andrew	
458.	W-242 Andrew—W-255 V. R.	
459.	W-255 Vance—W-265 Ida	
460.	W-265 Ignatz—W-300 James	
461.	W-300 James—W-300 William	
462.	W-300 William—W-323 Wm.	
463.	W-323 Wm.—W-340 Cora	
464.	W-340 Cristina—W-356 Hilbert	
465.	W-356 Hilda—W-400 Clothilde	

466. W-400 Clyde—W-410 Rudolph
467. W-410 Rudolph.—W-420 Erand
468. W-420 Eric—W-420 Michael
469. W-420 Michael—W-425 A. B.
470. W-425 A. B.—W-425 John
471. W-425 John—W-426 Frank
472. W-426 Frank—W-435 Chaney
473. W-435 Charles—W-450 Bernard
474. W-450 Bernard—W-452 Eunice
475. W-452 Eunice A.—W-452 Robert
476. W-452 Robert—W-460 Rusus
477. W-460 Ruth—W-523 Charles
478. W-523 Charles—W-536 Ces
479. W-536 Charles—W-600 Robert
480. W-600 Robert—W-623 Reuben
481. W-623 Reuben R.—W-632 Carrie
482. W-632 Catherine—W-655 H.
483. W-655 Harold A.—W-665 Wm. A.
484. X-100 Adam—X-652 Joe
485. Y-000—Y-520 Edward L.
486. Y-520 Edward M.—Y-620 Amos
487. Y-620 Anderson D.—Y-666 Frank
488. Z-000 Albert—Z-262 John W.
489. Z-262 Josef—Z-520 Nicholas
490. Z-520 Nick—Z-650 Donald
491. Z-650 Dorothy A.—Z-665 John

KANSAS   T1265   (Miracode)

1. A-000—A-346 Jhny H.
2. A-346 John—A-450 Dewitt C.
3. A-450 Dewitt C.—A-536 John A.
4. A-536 John A., Jr.—A-663 William A.
5. B-000—B-220 John W.
6. B-220 John W.—B-260 Dina
7. B-260 Dixon—B-340 Charles
8. B-340 Charles—B-400 William W.
9. B-400 Willie—B-450 David G.
10. B-450 David H.—B-520 Julius C.
11. B-520 Justin C.—B-560 Ed
12. B-560 Edna—B-620 J. Dick
13. B-620 J. F.—B-625 William W.
14. B-625 Willie—B-634 Frank S.
15. B-634 Frank S.—B-650 Frank E.
16. B-650 Frank E.—B-652 Henry
17. B-652 Henry—B-660 Charles W.
18. B-660 Charles W.—B-666 Luther
19. C-000—C-200 Clarenc E.
20. C-200 Clarence C.—C-256 Chas.
21. C-256 Clay—C-414 Rachel L.
22. C-414 Ranc—C-452 Harry C.
23. C-452 Harry D.—C-500 Clara
24. C-500 Clara—C-534 George L.
25. C-534 George W.—C-610 Michel F.
26. C-610 N. R.—C-624 J. L.
27. C-624 James—C-642 Albertina
28. C-642 Albin—C-665 Sam
29. D-000—D-130 Ezra
30. D-130 Ezra—D-250 George W.
31. D-250 George W.—D-400 Douglas
32. D-400 Dove E.—D-515 Willie L.
33. D-515 Wm. J.—D-560 Ray
34. D-560 Reuben—D-665 Orleese
35. E-000—E-300 Bernice
36. E-300 Bernice—E-451 Christene
37. E-451 David A.—E-665 Ida H.
38. F-000—F-320 Samuel
39. F-320 Samuel—F-455 Leer R.
40. F-455 Lena—F-616 Fannie E.
41. F-616 Flora—F-640 Robert
42. F-640 Robert—F-666 Ora M.
43. G-000—G-300 Joseph F.
44. G-300 Joseph H.—G-422 Porter
45. G-422 Ramay—G-532 John H.
46. G-532 Leroy—G-616 Ruth
47. G-616 Ruth—G-635 P. Sherman
48. G-635 Patrick M.—G-655 Otis
49. G-655 Patrick—G-666 Jose
50. H-000—H-163 Alva J.
51. H-163 Alvin H.—H-220 Josiphine
52. H-220 Katherine—H-252 Roy
53. H-252 Roy—H-325 Jauneta
54. H-325 Jeff—H-400 Joseph
55. H-400 Joseph—H-436 Frank
56. H-436 Frank—H-516 William
57. H-516 William—H-535 Wesley D.

58. H-535 Will—H-560 Shepherd
59. H-560 Silas W.—H-625 Harley
60. H-625 Harm—H-640 Samuel L.
61. H-640 Sarah—H-665 Mary
62. I-000—I-656 Pauline
63. J-000—J-500 Martinez
64. J-500 Marviae—J-523 Dora
65. J-523 Dora—J-525 Marie
66. J-525 Marion—J-666 John
67. K-000—K-325 Charles
68. K-325 Charles—K-456 Anna
69. K-456 Archibald—K-520 Udah
70. K-520 Ulisus—K-610 Joe
71. K-610 John—K-663 William
72. L-000—L-200 Charles
73. L-200 Charles—L-246 Fred
74. L-246 Fred—L-366 Ferdinand
75. L-366 George S.—L-520 Patrick
76. L-520 Patrick F.—L-552 Lorenzo D.
77. L-552 Lual—L-666 Gus
78. M-000—M-210 William C.
79. M-210 William E.—M-240 Benjamin F.
80. M-240 Benjamine F.—M-246 William
81. M-246 William—M-254 Richard
82. M-254 Richard—M-265 N. R.
83. M-265 N. R.—M-350 Pearl
84. M-350 Perley L.—M-460 Alice
85. M-460 Alice—M-500 Charlie
86. M-500 Charlie—M-553 James
87. M-553 Jose—M-600 William C.
88. M-600 William C.—M-622 Doler
89. M-622 Dorateo—M-635 H. C.
90. M-635 H. F.—M-665 Zack
91. N-000—N-320 Jacob
92. N-320 Jim—N-550 Ellen
93. N-550 Ellen E.—N-665 Leah
94. O-000—O-425 Albert
95. O-425 Albert—O-665 Oscar O.
96. P-000—P-300 Emms
97. P-300 Emma—P-362 Ola L.
98. P-362 Ola L.—P-452 Mary K.
99. P-452 Melvin—P-615 Benjaman
100. P-615 Bertie—P-625 Roy
101. P-625 Roy—P-666 Wesley B.
102. Q-000 C. W.—Q-663 Pic
103. R-000—R-160 Mary J.
104. R-160 Mary W.—R-200 Mary L.
105. R-200 Mary L.—R-255 Gottelib
106. R-255 Gottelib—R-300 Lydia A.
107. R-300 Lydia C.—R-362 Dale
108. R-362 Damiteo—R-520 William R.
109. R-520 William S.—R-662 Abunido
110. S-000—S-152 May
111. S-152 Melissa—S-200 John
112. S-200 John—S-300 Lyman L.
113. S-300 Lyman L.—S-320 Zerger J.
114. S-321 Andrew—S-350 Evaline
115. S-350 Everd E.—S-362 Horace
116. S-362 Ida—S-400 George
117. S-400 George—S-435 James M.
118. S-435 James M.—S-514 Mathew
119. S-514 Mathew—S-530 Clara
120. S-530 Clara—S-530 May
121. S-530 May—S-536 Justice
122. S-536 Kate—S-600 Ebn N.
123. S-600 Edith—S-640 William E.
124. S-640 William H.—S-666 Frank
125. T-000—T-400 Eve
126. T-400 Joeseph H.—T-512 Horace
127. T-512 Horace L.—T-555 John
128. T-555 Louis—T-652 Alexander H.
129. T-652 Alice—T-666 Matilda
130. U-000—U-662 Martin E.
131. V-000—V-535 Major H.
132. V-535 Marjarette—V-664 Theodore
133. W-000—W-236 Waldo H.
134. W-236 William—W-300 John M.
135. W-300 John M.—W-340 Anes B.
136. W-340 Anna—W-410 W. A.
137. W-410 W. W.—W-425 Elmer E.
138. W-425 Elmer E.—W-435 George
139. W-435 George—W-452 Russell
140. W-452 Russell B.—W-550 Walter F.
141. W-550 William—W-650 Ephrann
142. W-650 Ernest M.—W-665 Frank
143. X-136—X-643 Yaks B.

144. Y-000 Alice V.—Y-660 Yosa
145. Z-000—Z-660 Arthurn

KENTUCKY   T1266   (Miracode)

1. A-000—A-260 John
2. A-260 John—A-352 Mahala
3. A-352 Mahola—A-450 Abner
4. A-450 Abraham—A-536 Charlie
5. A-536 Charlie B.—A-653 H. G.
6. A-653 Haden—A-665 William B.
7. B-000—B-200 Thomas
8. B-200 Thomas—B-250 Aaron
9. B-250 Abby—B-260 Nettee
10. B-260 Neuton—B-340 John
11. B-340 John—B-400 Joseph
12. B-400 Joseph—B-420 Willie
13. B-420 Willie—B-452 Ennis
14. B-452 Enola—B-500 Liza
15. B-500 Liza—B-534 Keuns P.
16. B-534 Kusby S.—B-600 William S.
17. B-600 William S.—B-620 Robert E.
18. B-620 Robert E.—B-626 Frank S.
19. B-626 Frank W.—B-632 Lillie M.
20. B-632 Lindsay—B-636 George W.
21. B-636 George W.—B-650 Jerome
22. B-650 Jerome—B-652 Clyde
23. B-652 Clyde—B-653 Lou
24. B-653 Louan—B-663 Mat
25. B-663 Mc.—B-666 Nellie
26. C-000—C-160 Isaac
27. C-160 Isaac—C-200 Mattie
28. C-200 Mattie—C-252 Burnice C.
29. C-252 C. W.—C-400 John
30. C-400 John—C-430 William M.
31. C-430 William P.—C-452 Marion
32. C-452 Marion—C-462 George G.
33. C-462 George H.—C-512 Addaline
34. C-512 Aeminta—C-520 John W.
35. C-520 John W.—C-550 William E.
36. C-550 William E.—C-612 Sam
37. C-612 Sam—C-620 Leo J.
38. C-620 Leonard—C-632 Sara
39. C-632 Sara A.—C-640 Thad
40. C-640 Theodore—C-660 Robert
41. C-660 Robert—C-666 J. L.
42. D-000—D-120 Lulu
43. D-120 Lumbis—D-165 Charles H.
44. D-165 Courtney—D-252 Claud
45. D-252 Claude D.—D-362 Minnie
46. D-362 Nannie V.—D-500 Henry L.
47. D-500 Henry N.—D-525 Nannie
48. D-525 Nannie B.—D-600 Willie
49. D-600 Willie—D-665 Woodson
50. E-000—E-240 George
51. E-240 George—E-400 Louise
52. E-400 Lucinda—E-520 Conner
53. E-520 Connie T.—E-665 George R.
54. F-000—F-260 Louis
55. F-260 Louis—F-432 Edwin C.
56. F-432 Ela—F-500 Samuel
57. F-500 Samuel H.—F-623 Joe A.
58. F-623 Joe H.—F-645 Delia
59. F-645 Dennis A.—F-666 Wm. A.
60. G-000—G-200 G. W.
61. G-200 G. W.—G-355 Custon
62. G-355 Cynthia—G-426 G. A.
63. G-426 Gabriel—G-530 Aden
64. G-530 Adolf G.—G-612 Ora
65. G-612 Orville—G-626 Alphonse
66. G-626 Altie—G-650 Cornelius E.
67. G-650 Cornelus—G-653 Tithia
68. G-653 Todd—G-666 John
69. H-000—H-160 Linn B.
70. H-160 Lizzie—H-200 Pernelopa
71. H-200 Perry—H-240 E. J.
72. H-240 R. W.—H-260 Albert T.
73. H-260 Alex—H-322 Mary F.
74. H-322 Mary J.—H-400 Author
75. H-400 Author—H-400 Myrtle
76. H-400 Myrtle—H-431 Cecilia
77. H-431 Charles—H-500 Joseph B.
78. H-500 Joseph C.—H-522 James A.
79. H-522 James A.—H-536 Charles
80. H-536 Charles—H-552 William
81. H-552 William—H-620 Harry
82. H-620 Harry—H-630 Elen

83. H-630 Elhanen M.—H-635 Hiram
84. H-635 Hiram—H-655 Surahs W.
85. H-655 Susie—H-663 Mike
86. I-000—I-660 Elizabeth W.
87. J-000—J-250 Mary
88. J-250 Mary—J-520 Ella B.
89. J-520 Ella C.—J-520 Sam
90. J-520 Sam—J-525 George
91. J-525 George—J-525 Sarah
92. J-525 Sarah—J-660 William H.
93. K-000—K-350 Ballard
94. K-350 Bazil—K-465 Peter
95. K-465 William—K-523 George
96. K-523 George—K-620 Hiram
97. K-620 Hirram—K-662 Mary
98. L-000—L-152 John M.
99. L-152 John P.—L-200 Willaim
100. L-200 William—L-250 Will
101. L-250 Will—L-364 Louisa
102. L-364 Luince—L-520 Charles S.
103. L-520 Charles V.—L-534 Margarette M.
104. L-534 Marimilan—L-663 George
105. M-000—M-200 John H.
106. M-200 John H.—M-223 William
107. M-223 William D.—M-242 Edward
108. M-242 Edward—M-250 Lavina
109. M-250 Lawrence—M-255 C. G.
110. M-255 Carroll—M-265 George
111. M-265 George—M-324 Marion
112. M-324 Mark L.—M-420 Erma
113. M-420 Ernert—M-460 Alexander W.
114. M-460 Alferd—M-460 William E.
115. M-460 William E.—M-532 Tone
116. M-532 Toney—M-600 Henry C.
117. M-600 Henry C.—M-610 Louisa, Mrs.
118. M-610 Louise—M-623 R.
119. M-623 Robert E.—M-630 William F.
120. M-630 William James—M-640 J. Z.
121. M-640 Jack—M-665 Scott B.
122. N-000—N-250 John L.
123. N-250 John M.—N-453 Camilla
124. N-453 Camilla—N-660 Bill
125. O-000—O-340 John S.
126. O-340 John W.—O-612 John R.
127. O-612 Will—O-664 James W.
128. P-000—P-235 Carrie
129. P-235 Casilla—P-362 Alex
130. P-362 Alex—P-412 Eliza
131. P-412 Eliza—P-500 Hunter R.
132. P-500 Ida—P-600 Prior E.
133. P-600 R. T.—P-620 William C.
134. P-620 William C.—P-626 Martha
135. P-626 Martha—P-652 John D.
136. P-652 John P.—P-665 Burgess
137. Q-000 David C.—Q-660 Laura B.
138. R-000—R-152 Frank W.
139. R-152 Frank W.—R-163 Sattifield
140. R-163 Scott—R-200 Linch
141. R-200 Lincoln—R-240 Mary
142. R-240 Mary—R-263 Harry J.
143. R-263 Harry W.—R-320 Jim
144. R-320 Jim—R-400 Annie A.
145. R-400 Arch—R-512 Annie M.
146. R-512 Benj.—R-550 William T.
147. R-550 Willie E.—R-665 Asa C.
148. S-000—S-152 Bernard
149. S-152 Berry—S-163 Kattie
150. S-163 Kelse—S-241 Rosa L.
151. S-241 Roscoe—S-312 Harvey
152. S-312 Helen M.—S-322 Jim H.
153. S-322 Jimmie—S-346 Ed
154. S-346 Ed—S-354 Jeff D.
155. S-354 Jessee F.—S-363 Lorenza C.
156. S-363 Lorenzy C.—S-415 Josephine
157. S-415 Josephune—S-450 James
158. S-450 James—S-512 John
159. S-512 John A.—S-530 Armstrong
160. S-530 Armstrong—S-530 James H.
161. S-530 James H.—S-530 Sam B.
162. S-530 Sam C.—S-536 John
163. S-536 John—S-560 William
164. S-560 William—S-630 Malinda
165. S-630 Malissa—S-666 Oliver P.
166. T-000—T-260 Westly
167. T-260 Wilbur—T-460 Cassius

168. T-460 Catharine E.—T-500 John
169. T-500 John A.—T-520 George
170. T-520 George—T-553 Hettie
171. T-553 Louis B.—T-640 Ercey E.
172. T-640 Ernest—T-656 Sherman
173. T-656 Shirl—T-666 Melvin
174. U-000—U-656 Edward
175. V-000—V-524 Otho
176. V-524 Paul—V-664 Sofy
177. W-000—W-230 Lucille
178. W-230—W-300 Bruno
179. W-300 Brutes—W-300 Thomas
180. W-300 Thomas—W-325 Mollie
181. W-325 Mollie—W-360 Richard
182. W-360 Robert H.—W-420 Charles O.
183. W-420 Charles R.—W-425 A. B.
184. W-425 A. B.—W-425 Sudor Mrs.
185. W-425 Sue—W-436 Albert M.
186. W-436 Alex—W-452 Harry
187. W-452 Harry—W-460 Daniel M.
188. W-460 Daniel R.—W-614 Edward
189. W-614 Edward H.—W-640 James
190. W-640 James—W-666 Albert
191. X-100 George—X-653 Samuel
192. Y-000—Y-616 John
193. Y-616 John—Y-662 Sam H.
194. Z-000—Z-663 Adolph

LOUISIANA T1267 (Soundex)
See rolls 79–132 (Miracode) for New Orleans and Shreveport.

1. A-000—A-416 J.
2. A-416 K.—A-536 E.
3. A-536 F.—B-152
4. B-160—B-300 C.
5. B-300 D.—B-400 J.
6. B-400 K.—B-463 E.
7. B-463 F.—B-600 B.
8. B-600 C.—B-622 I.
9. B-622 J.—B-632
10. B-634—B-650 Ja
11. B-650 Je—B-653 J.
12. B-653 K.—C-200 O.
13. C-200 P.—C-410 M.
14. C-410 N.—C-460 L.
15. C-460 M.—C-540 L.
16. C-540 M.—C-630 M.
17. C-630 N.—D-000 L.
18. D-000 M.—D-145 J.
19. D-145 M.—D-250 J.
20. D-250 K.—D-500 V.
21. D-500 W.—D-626 D.
22. D-626 E.—E-420 C.
23. E-420 D.—F-420 B.
24. F-420 C.—F-622 C.
25. F-622 D.—F-656
26. G-000—G-360 T.
27. G-360 U.—G-520 M.
28. G-520 N.—G-630 J.
29. G-630 K.—G-656 D.
30. G-656 E.—H-235 I.
31. H-235 J.—H-400 F.
32. H-400 G.—H-513
33. H-520—H-560 I.
34. H-560 J.—H-630 G.
35. H-630 H.—J-210 A.
36. J-210 B.—J-251 G.
37. J-251 H.—J-520 Md
38. J-520 Me—J-525 Ha
39. J-525 He—J-526 J.
40. J-526 K.—K-520 Ji
41. K-520 Jo—L-100
42. L-110—L-200 G.
43. L-200 H.—L-260
44. L-300—L-530 J.
45. L-530 Jo—M-200 Ah
46. M-200 Al—M-240 M.
47. M-240 N.—M-264 I.
48. M-264 J.—M-420 Q.
49. M-420 R.—M-530
50. M-532—M-620 C.
51. M-620 D.—M-635 L.
52. M-635 M.—N-425 I.
53. N-425 J.—O-500 S.
54. O-500 T.—P-362 D.
55. P-362 E.—P-520 I.

56. P-520 J.—P-625 V.
57. P-625 W.—R-100 Q.
58. R-100 P.—R-163
59. R-164—R-263 Al
60. R-263 Am—R-400 L.
61. R-400 M.—S-140 C.
62. S-140 D.—S-300 P.
63. S-300 R.—S-363 C.
64. S-363 D.—S-460
65. S-500—S-530 Ha
66. S-530 He—S-536 K.
67. S-536 L.—S-651
68. T-000—T-460 G.
69. T-460 H.—T-520 Ji
70. T-520 Jo—T-650 K.
71. T-650 L.—V-525 G.
72. V-525 H.—W-252 K.
73. W-252 L.—W-325 E.
74. W-325 F.—W-420
75. W-425—W-436
76. W-450—W-452 Joe
77. W-452 Joh—W-530 I.
78. W-530 J.—Institutions

LOUISIANA CITIES: New Orleans and Shreveport

79. A-000 Albert—A-536 Whilemena
80. A-536 Wilelmina—A-665 George
81. B-000 Alfred J.—B-360 Louis
82. B-360 Louis—B-550 John
83. B-550 John—B-635 Robert D., Jr.
84. B-635 Robert H., Jr.—B-666 Irene
85. C-000—C-435 Robert
86. C-435 Robert L.—C-600 Mary
87. C-600 Mary—C-664 Mary
88. D-000 Adeline—D-300 Emma
89. D-300 Ernest—D-620 John
90. D-620 John—D-665 Lewis
91. E-000 Bittea—E-663 Viola A.
92. F-000 Abraham—F-620 Marie
93. F-620 Marie—F-666 Frank
94. G-000 A. J.—G-535 Louise
95. G-535 Menelas—G-665 Ophelia
96. H-000 Adolph—H-400 Myles
97. H-400 Myrtle—H-620 Era
98. H-620 Erie—H-663 Louise
99. I-000 Catherine—I-665 Frank
100. J-000 Annie C.—J-525 Charles
101. J-525 Charles—J-662 Harry
102. K-000 Adeline—K-634 Louis
103. K-634 Maud—K-663 Johanna
104. L-000 A.—L-250 George
105. L-250 George C.—L-566 Jane
106. L-600 Abraham—L-663 Charles
107. M-000 Anna—M-256 Geo. H.
108. M-256 George—M-462 Forest
109. M-462 Franceska—M-620 Rosehen
110. M-620 Rosey—M-665 Marion
111. N-000 Adolph MD—N-662 August
112. O-000 Chas.—O-663 Irene
113. P-000 AH—P-520 Rawley M.
114. P-520 Roland—P-666 Eligh
115. Q-000 Hari KEW—Q-652 William J.
116. R-000 Abe—R-256 Bryan
117. R-256 Casper—R-560 Thomas
118. R-560 Virginia—R-660 Rene
119. S-000 Adele—S-320 Eugene, Mrs.
120. S-320 Florence—S-500 Harrison
121. S-500 Harry—S-550 John
122. S-550 John—S-666 Paul
123. T-000 Alice—T-620 Jacob
124. T-620 Jake—T-663 Paul
125. U-100 Leon—U-652 Zoba
126. V-000 Albert—V-665 Grace
127. W-000 Antoinet—W-410 Ernest
128. W-410 Ernestine—W-452 Sam
129. W-452 Sam—W-663 Gertrude
130. X-140 Robert—X-660 Laura
131. Y-000 Huey—Y-656 Elberka
132. Z-000 Clara—Z-655 Nelie

MICHIGAN T1268 (Miracode)

1. A-000—A-235 Lulu
2. A-235 Lydia—A-352 Helen
3. A-352 Helen—A-432 William S.
4. A-433 Bertha M.—A-516 Margaret

5.	A-516 Martha—A-536 Fredrick F.
6.	A-536 Fredricka—A-623 Peter
7.	A-623 Philinda—A-665 William
8.	B-000—B-200 Franklin P.
9.	B-200 Fred—B-216 Mary E.
10.	B-216 Mary E.—B-242 Fred
11.	B-242 Fred—B-260 Charlie
12.	B-260 Charlie—B-300 Irving W.
13.	B-300 Irwin—B-346 Arthur
14.	B-346 Arthur—B-400 Fredrick
15.	B-400 Fredrick—B-420 Jennie
16.	B-420 Jennie E.—B-432 Matthew
17.	B-432 Matthew—B-453 Lizzie M.
18.	B-453 Lloyd J.—B-516 Phillip
19.	B-516 Ralph E.—B-530 Irvine J.
20.	B-530 Isa—B-552 Octive
21.	B-552 Otto—B-612 Mark
22.	B-612 Mary—B-620 Ida
23.	B-620 Ida—B-622 Pauline
24.	B-622 Pauling—B-626 Ed
25.	B-626 Eden W.—B-632 Anna L.
26.	B-632 Annie—B-635 James J.
27.	B-635 James J.—B-650 Cornelus
28.	B-650 Cortez—B-650 Roy
29.	B-650 Roy—B-652 Rose
30.	B-652 Rose B.—B-655 William
31.	B-655 William—B-666 Samuel J.
32.	C-000—C-155 Robert
33.	C-155 Robert—C-200 John
34.	C-200 John—C-245 John
35.	C-245 John—C-350 Henry
36.	C-350 Henry E.—C-412 Henry
37.	C-412 Henry—C-435 Harry A.
38.	C-435 Harry A.—C-455 Thomas
39.	C-455 Thomas—C-463 Adolph
40.	C-463 Adrian C.—C-514 Murdock
41.	C-514 Myron—C-535 George F.
42.	C-535 Georgia—C-565 Ross
43.	C-565 Ruby—C-615 Manson
44.	C-615 Maragret—C-623 Emma
45.	C-623 Emma—C-632 William J.
46.	C-632 William J.—C-642 Marth C.
47.	C-642 Martha—C-654 William H.
48.	C-654 William J.—C-656 Fred
49.	D-000 A. J.—D-120 John
50.	D-120 John—D-153 Josephine
51.	D-153 Josie—D-234 Damos
52.	D-234 David—D-260 Frank
53.	D-260 Frank—D-350 Johanna
54.	D-350 John—D-430 Noah
55.	D-430 Oscar—D-500 Louis
56.	D-500 Louis F.—D-525 Burs
57.	D-525 Burt W.—D-552 Frederick
58.	D-552 Fredia—D-620 Frederick
59.	D-620 Frederick—D-652 Gaisowes
60.	D-652 George—D-665 Urbin
61.	E-000—E-240 Seymour C.
62.	E-240 Solemon—E-363 Frank
63.	E-363 Frank—E-452 Jake
64.	E-452 Jake—E-624 Andrew
65.	E-624 Andrew—E-664 Frank
66.	F-000—F-236 George
67.	F-236 George—F-321 Raymond
68.	F-321 Richard—F-432 Ena
69.	F-432 Enoch—F-462 Alfred M.
70.	F-462 Alison—F-600 Joseph
71.	F-600 Joseph—F-623 Vernon
72.	F-623 Vesta—F-640 Mary
73.	F-640 Mary—F-655 Charles H.
74.	F-655 Charles J.—F-666 Jeanette
75.	G-000—G-200 Minnie
76.	G-200 Minnie E.—G-320 Fred
77.	G-320 Fred—G-400 Lydia
78.	G-400 Lydia M. S.—G-426 Patrick
79.	G-426 Patrick—G-500 Bennie
80.	G-500 Bernardo—G-600 George W.
81.	G-600 George W.—G-616 Levi A.
82.	G-616 Lewis—G-626 John
83.	G-626 John—G-650 Alfred N.
84.	G-650 Alfred R.—G-652 Everett
85.	G-652 Ezra—G-666 Lida B.
86.	H-000—H-152 William
87.	H-152 William—H-200 Carl
88.	H-200 Carl—H-200 Wm. H.
89.	H-200 Wm. H.—H-241 Alexander
90.	H-241 Alfred—H-256 Earl
91.	H-256 Eddie—H-320 Franklin

92.	H-320 Fred—H-356 Frank
93.	H-356 Fred—H-400 Leo
94.	H-400 Leo—H-423 Katie B.
95.	H-423 L. D.—H-452 Harriet
96.	H-452 Harriett—H-514 Beanthia
97.	H-514 Earl—H-525 Clara
98.	H-525 Clara—H-536 Emil
99.	H-536 Emil—H-553 Claud
100.	H-553 Claud—H-616
101.	H-616 Mary—H-626 William
102.	H-626 William—H-635 Everett J.
103.	H-635 Everett—H-655 Edward
104.	H-655 Edward—H-665 Richard
105.	I-000—I-664 Myrtle
106.	J-000—J-250 Bert
107.	J-250 Bert C.—J-520 August
108.	J-520 August—J-523 Earl
109.	J-523 Earl—J-525 Godfrey A.
110.	J-525 Goel—J-525 Vern A.
111.	J-525 Vern E.—J-665 William
112.	K-000—K-200 Franz
113.	K-200 Franz—K-252 Homas
114.	K-252 Ida—K-360 Victor
115.	K-360 Virgil—K-420 George
116.	K-420 George—K-452 Joseph
117.	K-452 Joseph—K-510 Fred
118.	K-510 Fred—K-520 Philip
119.	K-520 Philip—K-532 John J.
120.	K-532 John N.—K-613 August
121.	K-613 Augusta—K-626 J. Nelson
122.	K-626 Jacob—K-656 Samond
123.	K-656 Samuel—K-666 Mathew J.
124.	L-000—L-130 Sam
125.	L-130 Sam—L-163 Alice
126.	L-163 Aloysious—L-200 Loise
127.	L-200 Lola—L-236 Mary M.
128.	L-236 Matilda—L-300 Henry
129.	L-300 Henry—L-360 August
130.	L-360 August—L-510 Andrew
131.	L-510 Andrew—L-520 Louis
132.	L-520 Louis—L-531 John
133.	L-531 John—L-560 Katie
134.	L-560 Konstanly—L-625 William
135.	L-625 William—L-665 Violet
136.	M-000—M-200 John K.
137.	M-200 John L.—M-220 Arthur
138.	M-220 Arthur—M-235 Lea
139.	M-235 Lee—M-242 Henery
140.	M-242 Hengh—M-246 Joseph
141.	M-246 Jospeh C.—M-252 Jane
142.	M-252 Jason H.—M-255 John
143.	M-255 John—M-263 Anna J.
144.	M-263 Anna M.—M-320 Arthur R.
145.	M-320 Arthur W.—M-326 Harrison
146.	M-326 Harry—M-420 George W.
147.	M-420 George W.—M-452 John
148.	M-452 John—M-460 John
149.	M-460 John—M-500 Mark H.
150.	M-500 Marry—M-532 Jesse
151.	M-532 Jesse—M-600 Bessie
152.	M-600 Bessie—M-600 Truman
153.	M-600 Tryphane—M-620 Gladys M.
154.	M-620 Gleason—M-620 John R.
155.	M-624 John S.—M-633 Silas
156.	M-633 Thomas—M-640 William H.
157.	M-640 William H.—M-665 Oscar
158.	N-000—N-232 Edward
159.	N-232 Frank—N-324 Louis H.
160.	N-324 Louisa—N-425 Ralph
161.	N-425 Ralph H.—N-622 Albert
162.	N-622 Alex—N-663 Harrison
163.	O-000—O-240 Ben
164.	O-240 Ben B.—O-423 Oscar
165.	O-423 Peter—O-550 Frank
166.	O-550 Frank—O-666 Audrey
167.	P-000—P-200 Sall
168.	P-200 Sallie—P-263 Ida
169.	P-263 Ida—P-360 Frederick
170.	P-360 Frederick C.—P-362 Peter
171.	P-362 Peter—P-412 Patrick H.
172.	P-412 Paul—P-450 Selden B.
173.	P-450 Selina—P-521 Harvey J.
174.	P-521 Henderson—P-615 Joseph
175.	P-615 Laffata—P-622 Henry
176.	P-622 Henry—P-626 Harry
177.	P-626 Harry—P-642 Richard
178.	P-642 Robert—P-666 Meyer

179.	Q-000 Adelbert—Q-662 Vicenzo
180.	R-000—R-145 Fred C.
181.	R-145 Fred M.—R-163 Jennie
182.	R-163 Jennie—R-200 Ida S.
183.	R-200 Idus—R-220 Matt
184.	R-220 Max—R-250 Frank J.
185.	R-250 Frank L.—R-262 Sara M.
186.	R-262 Sarah—R-300 Jay G.
187.	R-300 Jay L.—R-340 Charles O.
188.	R-340 Charles T.—R-400 Oscar
189.	R-400 Oscar E.—R-516 Agnes
190.	R-516 Alah—R-536 Mary
191.	R-536 Minnie—R-630 Abraham
192.	R-630 Adolph—R-663 Amedie
193.	S-000—S-126 Paul
194.	S-126 Paul—S-152 Mary, Mrs.
195.	S-152 Mary S.—S-163 Beatrice
196.	S-163 Beckie—S-215 Rosa
197.	S-215 Sadie—S-260 Frank
198.	S-260 Frank—S-310 George
199.	S-310 George—S-316 Marie L.
200.	S-316 Marillda J.—S-326 William
201.	S-326 William—S-346 Peter
202.	S-346 Philemon—S-353 Harvey B.
203.	S-353 Hattie—S-362 James C.
204.	S-362 James D.—S-365 Albert J.
205.	S-365 Albert L.—S-412 Lewis H.
206.	S-412 Lilian—S-425 George
207.	S-426 George F.—S-450 Elizabeth
208.	S-450 Elizabeth—S-500 Richard E.
209.	S-500 Richard J.—S-521 Walter W.
210.	S-521 Wilber—S-530 Chancy
211.	S-530 Chancy—S-530 Henry
212.	S-530 Henry—S-530 Otto A.
213.	S-530 Otto A. A.—S-536 Alberta
214.	S-536 Albertina—S-543 Sarah
215.	S-543 Settie—S-561 John
216.	S-561 John—S-620 Geo. S.
217.	S-620 George—S-636 Herman J.
218.	S-636 Herman L.—S-666 Warren
219.	T-000—T-236 Perry
220.	T-236 Ralph—T-400 Maria
221.	T-400 Martha—T-460 Tilden I.
222.	T-460 Tillie—T-514 William
223.	T-514 William—T-545 Jennie
224.	T-545 Jennie—T-620 Ellie E.
225.	T-620 Elma H.—T-651 Henry
226.	T-651 Henry—T-666 Alfred
227.	U-000—U-663 R. Bernie
228.	V-000—V-430 Jerome
229.	V-430 Jessie C.—V-524 Willmer
230.	V-524 Wilson—V-536 Johannes
231.	V-536 Johanus—V-635 William
232.	V-635 William K.—V-666 Mitton L.
233.	W-000—W-200 Katherine
234.	W-200 Katherine—W-240 Mary Ann
235.	W-240 Mary E.—W-265 Eugene A.
236.	W-265 Frank N.—W-300 Scott
237.	W-300 Scott—W-326 William J.
238.	W-326 William K.—W-362 John P.
239.	W-362 John W.—W-420 Alvernon D.
240.	W-420 Alvin—W-422 Clarence A.
241.	W-422 Clarence E.—W-425 Robert
242.	W-425 Robert—W-436 Bertha
243.	W-436 Bertha—W-452 John
244.	W-452 John—W-520 Andrew
245.	W-520 Andrew—W-600 Abraham
246.	W-600 Addie M.—W-630 George W.
247.	W-630 George W.—W-656 Samuel
248.	W-656 Samuel—W-663 Leo
249.	X-000—X-650 Henry
250.	Y-000—Y-600 Briget
251.	Y-600 Catherine—Y-663 Wilnerva
252.	Z-000 Abraham—Z-565 Lide M.
253.	Z-565 Lillie—Z-665 Lambertes

MISSISSIPPI T1269 (Soundex)

1.	A-000—A-352 L.
2.	A-352 M.—A-450 V.
3.	A-450 W.—A-600 S.
4.	A-600 T.—B-200
5.	B-210—B-260 Jessie M.
6.	B-260 Jim—B-346
7.	B-350—B-420 H.
8.	B-420 I.—B-454

9.	B-460—B-530 V.
10.	B-530 W.—B-620 I.
11.	B-620 J.—B-630 F.
12.	B-630 G.—B-635
13.	B-636—B-650 Johns
14.	B-650 John—B-652 E.
15.	B-652 F.—B-656
16.	B-660—C-200 G.
17.	C-200 H.—C-330
18.	C-340—C-425
19.	C-430—C-455 J.
20.	C-455 K.—C-500 V.
21.	C-500 W.—C-552 V.
22.	C-552 W.—C-620 K.
23.	C-620 L.—C-636 L.
24.	C-636 M.—D-100
25.	D-120—D-120 R.
26.	D-120 S.—D-250 C.
27.	D-250 D.—D-450
28.	D-452—D-540
29.	D-541—E-152 D.
30.	E-152 E.—E-363 F.
31.	E-363 G.—E-650
32.	F-000—F-430
33.	F-432—F-600
34.	F-610—F-652 F.
35.	F-652 G.—G-200 Q.
36.	G-200 R.—G-420
37.	G-421—G-560
38.	G-600—G-620
39.	G-621—G-650 H.
40.	G-650 I.—H-000
41.	H-100—H-200 U.
42.	H-200 V.—H-260
43.	H-261—H-400 B.
44.	H-400 C.—H-414
45.	H-416—H-500
46.	H-510—H-536 C.
46A.	H-536 D.—H-610 G.
47.	H-610 H.—H-620 Rilous
48.	H-620 Rita—H-631
49.	H-632—I-200
50.	I-300—J-250 G.
51.	J-250 H.—J-520 A.
52.	J-520 B.—J-520 K.
53.	J-520 L.—J-520 Z.
54.	No roll exists for this number.
55.	J-522 A.—J-525 I.
56.	J-525 J.—J-525 Shoe
57.	J-525 Si—K-230
58.	K-240—K-520 I.
59.	K-520 J.—L-000 Ary
60.	L-000 Asa—L-152 I.
61.	L-152 J.—L-220
62.	L-230—L-350
63.	L-352—L-525 K.
64.	L-525 L.—M-143 K.
65.	M-143 L.—M-200 Wh
66.	M-200 Wi—M-240 C.
67.	M-240 D.—M-246 J.
68.	M-246 K.—M-254 J.
69.	M-254 K.—M-320 C.
70.	M-320 D.—M-420 I.
71.	M-420 J.—M-460 S.
72.	M-460 T.—M-600 Bl
73.	M-600 Bo—M-610 F.
74.	M-610 G.—M-625 M.
75.	M-625 N.—N-160
76.	N-200—N-425 D.
77.	N-425 E.—O-300
78.	O-340—P-200 E.
79.	P-200 F.—P-355 M.
80.	P-355 N.—P-420 D.
81.	P-420 E.—P-610
82.	P-612—P-625
83.	P-626—P-654
84.	P-655—R-152 K.
85.	R-152 L.—R-200 A.
86.	R-200 B.—R-250 E.
87.	R-250 F.—R-300 J.
88.	R-300 K.—R-420 D.
89.	R-420 E.—R-562
90.	R-600—S-163 E.
91.	S-163 F.—S-300 Q.
92.	S-300 R.—S-340 E.
93.	S-340 F.—S-363 F.
94.	S-363 G.—S-420 I.

95.	S-420 J.—S-520 E.
96.	S-520 F.—S-530 Fos
97.	S-530 Fr.—S-530 Per
98.	S-530 Pet—S-536 M.
99.	S-536 N.—S-616
100.	S-620—T-300 J.
101.	T-300 K.—T-460 Ll
102.	T-460 Lo—T-514 Q.
103.	T-514 R.—T-525 D.
104.	T-525 E.—T-652
105.	T-653—V-300
106.	V-400—W-230
107.	W-231—W-300 D.
108.	W-300 E.—W-320 El
109.	W-320 Em—W-350 I.
110.	W-350 J.—W-420 F.
111.	W-420 G.—W-425 Js
112.	W-425 Ju—W-426
113.	W-430—W-452 C.
114.	W-452 D.—W-452 La
115.	W-452 Le—W-452
116.	W-453—W-620
117.	W-623—W-651
118.	W-656—Inst.

MISSOURI T1270 (Miracode)

1.	A-000—A-235 Editha
2.	A-235 Edna—A-340 Isabel
3.	A-340 J. F.—A-416 Aquilino
4.	A-416 Archie A.—A-450 Adalia
5.	A-450 Adaline—A-520 Mayme E.
6.	A-520 Michael—A-536 Mary
7.	A-536 Mary—A-652 George M.
8.	A-652 George W.—A-665 Richard B.
9.	B-000—B-200 George P.
10.	B-200 George P.—B-216 Clarence
11.	B-216 Claud—B-242 Lizzie
12.	B-242 Louis—B-260 Archy
13.	B-260 Ardellia—B-262 Bernard H.
14.	B-262 Bessie—B-320 Mary J.
15.	B-320 Mary L.—B-361 Vincent
16.	B-361 Walter—B-400 R. N.
17.	B-400 R.—B-420 Robert L.
18.	B-420 Robert L.—B-435 Elmer
19.	B-435 Elmer C.—B-453 Herry
20.	B-453 Hiram H.—B-500 Mary
21.	B-500 Mary—B-526 Gustav
22.	B-526 H. H.—B-550 Domenica
23.	B-550 Don—B-600 Henrietta
24.	B-600 Henrt—B-620 Annie B.
25.	B-620 Annie C.—B-620 Mary
26.	B-620 Mary—B-623 Laura T.
27.	B-623 Laura V.—B-626 Francis
28.	B-626 Francis—B-630 Rosco
29.	B-630 Rose—B-634 Samuel S.
30.	B-634 Samuel S.—B-642 Frak
31.	B-642 Francis A.—B-650 Harry
32.	B-650 Harry—B-650 Robert Lee
33.	B-650 Robert M.—B-652 J. H.
34.	B-652 J. H.—B-653 John
35.	B-653 John—B-656 Gustave
36.	B-656 Gustaves A.—B-666 Walter E.
37.	C-000—C-155 Arthur
38.	C-155 Arthur—C-200 Edward L.
39.	C-200 Edward M.—C-200 William H.
40.	C-200 William H.—C-260 George
41.	C-260 George—C-365 Cora S.
42.	C-365 Deak—C-415 John
43.	C-415 John—C-435 Edith B.
44.	C-435 Edmond—C-452 Roger H.
45.	C-452 Roland—C-462 Elizabeth
46.	C-462 Elizabeth A.—C-500 John
47.	C-500 John—C-514 Sarah
48.	C-514 Sarah—C-536 George W.
49.	C-536 Gerorge—C-560 Patrick H.
50.	C-560 Patrick P.—C-613 Mariah
51.	C-613 Mariah C.—C-620 Joseph
52.	C-620 Joseph—C-625 John
53.	C-625 John—C-636 Dela
54.	C-636 Delia—C-642 Carl E.
55.	C-642 Carl F.—C-654 Harry M.
56.	C-654 Hattie—C-665 Will
57.	D-000—D-120 Guy E.
58.	D-120 Guy O.—D-125 Katherine
59.	D-125 Kathryn—D-200 Albert

60.	D-200 Albert—D-250 Anna
61.	D-250 Anna—D-263 Arthur
62.	D-263 Arthur—D-360 George W.
63.	D-360 Geroge—D-432 Joseph
64.	D-432 Lyman—D-500 Lewis, Sr.
65.	D-500 Lewis T.—D-525 Henry O.
66.	D-525 Henry S.—D-550 Gale
67.	D-550 Geneva W.—D-620 Beatrice
68.	D-620 Bell—D-652 Harry M.
69.	D-652 Hary—D-666 Henry
70.	E-000—E-166 Peter
71.	E-166 Peter—E-262 Minerva
72.	E-262 Myron—E-363 Nancy J.
73.	E-363 Narcissy J.—E-430 Mary Alice
74.	E-430 Mary C.—E-524 Thomas
75.	E-524 Thomas—E-666 Frances M.
76.	F-000—F-236 Jasper
77.	F-236 Jeff Rob—F-316 Anthony F.
78.	F-320 A. J.—F-425 Hattie E.
79.	F-425 Hazel—F-453 Clarence
80.	F-453 Clarence—F-520 Robert M.
81.	F-520 Robert M.—F-615 Harold
82.	F-615 Henry—F-624 J. A.
83.	F-624 Jack—F-636 Karl
84.	F-636 Karl B.—F-652 Sadie
85.	F-652 Salvesta—F-666 Peter
86.	G-000—G-163 J. H.
87.	G-163 Jackson—G-300 Earl S.
88.	G-300 Earnest—G-356 Charles
89.	G-356 Charles—G-420 Nicke
90.	G-420 Noah—G-450 Anthony
91.	G-450 Antonio—G-520 Jessie
92.	G-520 Jessie H.—G-600 Julius
93.	G-600 Julius—G-615 James
94.	G-615 James—G-622 Kiligu
95.	G-622 Lanoa—G-632 Mareke
96.	G-632 Margarette—G-650 Eliza
97.	G-650 Eliza—G-652 Mary
98.	G-652 Mary—G-666 Henrietta Cass
99.	H-000—H-145 Edward A.
100.	H-145 Edward H.—H-163 Dausy
101.	H-163 Dave—H-200 John
102.	H-200 John—H-220 Josephd
103.	H-220 Josephine—H-243 William L.
104.	H-243 William S.—H-252 Thomas C.
105.	H-252 Thomas C.—H-300 James
106.	H-300 James—H-325 J. M.
107.	H-325 J. T.—H-364 Roland M.
108.	H-364 Samuel J.—H-400 John
109.	H-400 John—H-416 John D.
110.	H-416 John R.—H-435 Ellae H.
111.	H-435 Ellis—H-455 James L.
112.	H-455 James M.—H-514 Fred
113.	H-514 Fred—H-522 George E.
114.	H-522 George F.—H-530 Ruby M.
115.	H-530 Rufus E.—H-536 William F.
116.	H-536 William F.—H-560 Arthur S.
117.	H-560 Arthur T.—H-616 Armstead
118.	H-616 Art—H-620 William G.
119.	H-620 William G.—H-630 Geo. N.
120.	H-630 Geo. W.—H-635 Elma
121.	H-635 Elmer—H-651 Norval
122.	H-651 Oler—H-666 S. J.
123.	I-000—I-665 Benjamin
124.	J-000—J-250 Buelah
125.	J-250 Burrell—J-400 Joseph
126.	J-400 Joseph C.—J-520 Goerge B.
127.	J-520 Goerge W.—J-520 Standich
128.	J-520 Stanislaus—J-525 David
129.	J-525 David—J-525 Lucille
130.	J-525 Lucille—J-552 Thaddeus
131.	J-552 Thelma—J-663 William
132.	K-000—K-200 William
133.	K-200 William—K-300 Robert
134.	K-300 Robert—K-400 Katherine
135.	K-400 Katherine—K-450 Augusta
136.	K-450 Augustine—K-500 Fa
137.	K-500 Fannie—K-520 Dave
138.	K-520 Dave—K-524 George
139.	K-524 George B.—K-550 John
140.	K-550 John—K-620 Theodore
141.	K-620 Theodore—K-650 William F.
142.	K-650 William F.—K-666 Robert
143.	L-000—L-116 Helen
144.	L-116 Henry J.—L-163 Frank
145.	L-163 Frank—L-200 Louis H.
146.	L-200 Louis L.—L-236 Andy

147. L-236 Anna—L-260 Mattie P.
148. L-260 Maud—L-350 George
149. L-350 George—L-500 George E.
150. L-500 George E.—L-520 Eliza
151. L-520 Eliza—L-523 Stella M.
152. L-523 Stnley M.—L-540 Henry
153. L-540 Henry W.—L-616 Fred
154. L-616 Frederick I.—L-666 Hattie M.
155. M-000—M-200 Elmira J.
156. M-200 Elma—M-210 Anna L.
157. M-210 Annetta—M-225 Calude
158. M-225 Ceota—M-236 Katy
159. M-236 Laren—M-242 Mike
160. M-242 Mike—M-246 William P.
161. M-246 William R.—M-252 Ewell
162. M-252 Ezra—M-255 Florence E.
163. M-255 Flornec—M-261 Thomas
164. M-261 Thomas—M-300 Herbert W.
165. M-300 Herman—M-324 Henry
166. M-324 Henry—M-354 Chas. L.
167. M-354 Edd—M-425 C. A.
168. M-425 Carl—M-460 Amelia
169. M-460 Amelia—M-460 John
170. M-460 John—M-500 B. Lucien
171. M-500 B. Lucien—M-524 Ema B.
172. M-524 Emanuel—M-552 John
173. M-552 John—M-600 Floyd C.
174. M-600 Floyd M.—M-600 McHenry
175. M-600 McKinley—M-610 Thomas
176. M-610 Thomas—M-620 Kale
177. M-620 Kalip—M-624 William
178. M-624 William—M-633 Geo.
179. M-633 George—M-635 Thomas
180. M-635 Thomas—M-666 John
181. N-000—N-236 Allie
182. N-236 Andrew W.—N-342 Charles T.
183. N-342 Charles T.—N-425 John J.
184. N-425 John J.—N-600 George
185. N-600 George B.—N-665 Joseph W.
186. O-000—O-235 Neal
187. O-235 Ollie—O-410 Elisa
188. O-410 Elmer G.—O-540 John J.
189. O-540 John J.—O-665 William H.
190. P-000—P-200 John
191. P-200 John—P-300 David
192. P-300 David—P-360 Eliza
193. P-360 Elizabeth—P-400 B. H.
194. P-400 Ban—B-412 Thomas
195. P-412 Thomas—P-455 Lizzie
196. P-455 Lloyd—P-525 Joshua
197. P-525 Julia—P-614 Steve
198. P-614 Susan—P-620 Sarah J.
199. P-620 Sarah J.—P-625 Sylvester
200. P-625 Sylvester E.—P-636 Charles
201. P-636 Charles—P-666 Louis P.
202. Q-000—Q-662 William
203. R-000—R-125 Jom
204. R-125 Joseph—R-152 Zachanish
205. R-152 Zachriah C.—R-163 William
206. R-163 William—R-200 John
207. R-200 John—R-230 August
208. R-230 Augusta—R-250 Howard
209. R-250 Howard—R-262 Lula
210. R-262 Lula—R-300 Guy
211. R-300 Guy—R-320 Thomas
212. R-320 Thomas—R-356 Wm.
213. R-356 Wm.—R-423 Fannie
214. R-423 Forest—R-511 Henry
215. R-512 A. J.—R-534 Rilett
216. R-534 Robert—R-620 William
217. R-620 William C.—R-665 George A.
218. S-000—S-123 William
219. S-123 William—S-152 Joab
220. S-152 Jobac—S-162 Francis
221. S-162 Francis—S-200 Emma
222. S-200 Emma—S-245 Filipa
223. S-245 Fred C.—S-300 James
224. S-300 James—S-315 Charles
225. S-315 Charles—S-320 Henry J.
226. S-320 Henry J.—S-330 James
227. S-330 James—S-344 Essie
228. S-344 Fay—S-351 William N.
229. S-351 William N.—S-360 Oscar F.
230. S-360 Oscar T.—S-363 Frank J.
231. S-363 Frank K.—S-365 Samuel
232. S-365 Samuel—S-415 Patrick F.

233. S-415 Patrick H.—S-432 Frances
234. S-432 Frances—S-453 William J.
235. S-453 Willie—S-500 William
236. S-500 William—S-520 Mecella
237. S-520 Mell—S-530 August
238. S-530 August—S-530 George
239. S-530 George—S-530 Lawrence C.
240. S-530 Lawrence E.—S-530 Thomas A.
241. S-530 Thomas A.—S-536 Clarence L.
242. S-536 Clarence T.—S-540 Samuel L.
243. S-540 Samuel W.—S-560 John
244. S-560 John—S-610 Theo B.
245. S-610 Theodore—S-632 Albert
246. S-632 Albert—S-656 Victoria
247. S-656 Vielor—S-665 Thodore
248. T-000—T-250 John H.
249. T-250 John H.—T-360 Haston
250. T-360 Henry—T-460 Ethel
251. T-460 Ethel—T-512 Carrei
252. T-512 Carrie—T-520 Claud H.
253. T-520 Claude—T-525 Wiford
254. T-525 Wilbert—T-612 William H.
255. T-612 William H.—T-640 Stevewll
256. T-640 Susan—T-656 Joseph
257. T-656 Josephine—T-666 William
258. U-000—U-663 Thos. R.
259. V-000—V-400 Clinton E.
260. V-400 Colen—V-531 Lucy
261. V-531 Maggie—V-665 John
262. W-000—W-200 Edwin R.
263. W-200 Effa—W-236 Elizah W.
264. W-236 Ellen—W-256 Margaret I.
265. W-256 Margaretha—W-300 James
266. W-300 James—W-320 Bert
267. W-320 Bert—W-325 Madie
268. W-325 Magdelena—W-355 William
269. W-355 William—W-400 Susan Y.
270. W-400 Susana—W-420 Genevive E.
271. W-420 Genjamin K.—W-422 Charles P.
272. W-422 Charles S.—W-425 Kate
273. W-425 Kate—W-425 John W.
274. W-426 John W.—W-436 Julia
275. W-436 Julia—W-452 F. B.
276. W-452 F. E.—W-452 Rolla
277. W-452 Rolla—W-500 Robert
278. W-500 Robert—W-536 Paul G.
279. W-536 Pauline—W-623 Kattie
280. W-623 Kenneth C.—W-640 Nathaniel A.
281. W-640 Nurses—W-664 Eliza J.
282. X-000—X-612 Lindsey
283. Y-000—Y-520 Sophia
284. Y-520 Sophie—Y-660 Warren
285. Z-000 Adolph—Z-662 Bernard

NORTH CAROLINA   T1271 (Miracode)

1. A-000—A-263 Thomas W.
2. A-263 Tom—A-420 Terl
3. A-420 Thomas D.—A-450 George W.
4. A-450 George W.—A-536 Henreta S.
5. A-536 Henrietta—A-653 Thomas R.
6. A-653 Utley—A-663 Mary M.
7. B-000—B-214 Luis
8. B-214 Maurry—B-255 Adam
9. B-255 Adam—B-300 Junior
10. B-300 Junis—B-355 Lima
11. B-355 Lindsey—B-415 John M.
12. B-415 John M.—B-425 McDaniel
13. B-425 Melvin Henry—B-455 Washington
14. B-455 William—B-520 Goldie
15. B-520 Goldman B.—B-540 Polly A.
16. B-540 Rachel—B-616 Purch
17. B-616 R. H.—B-622 Thomas
18. B-622 Thomas C.—B-630 Joh T.
19. B-630 John—B-635 Carrie
20. B-635 Carrie—B-650 Enoch F.
21. B-650 Enoch S.—B-650 Rufus
22. B-650 Rufus—B-652 Rosa M.
23. B-652 Rosco—B-655 Bird
24. B-655 Bob—B-666 Catherine
25. C-000—C-152 Will
26. C-152 Will—C-200 Lafayatte

27. C-200 Lea A.—C-263 Pender W.
28. C-263 Rachel—C-400 Martha
29. C-400 Martha F.—C-436 William
30. C-436 William—C-462 Earley
31. C-462 Earlie—C-514 James
32. C-514 James—C-550 Lenrel H.
33. C-550 Leslie—C-613 Sam
34. C-613 Samuel—C-620 Wesley
35. C-620 Wesley J.—C-636 Daniel
36. C-636 Daniel—C-651 Amzy
37. C-651 Andy—C-665 Nancy
38. D-000—D-120 John W.
39. D-120 John W.—D-152 William D.
40. D-152 William L.—D-250 Rufus
41. D-250 Rufus—D-400 Tilus
42. D-400 Titus—D-520 William
43. D-520 William—D-620 Al
44. D-620 Albert—D-665 T. I.
45. E-000—E-250 Lawrence
46. E-250 Loyd—E-363 Richard
47. E-363 Richard H.—E-514 Hardy
48. E-514 Henry—E-663 Zebulan B.
49. F-000—F-260 Mildred L.
50. F-260 Mildred L.—F-433 James
51. F-433 John—F-540 Mack
52. F-540 Mada—F-630 F. T.
53. F-630 Fannie—F-655 Jency
54. F-655 Jenie—F-665 Willis
55. G-000—G-300 Emma
56. G-300 Emma E.—G-410 MM
57. G-410 Maggie—G-500 Ida
58. G-500 Ida M.—G-612 Robert
59. G-612 Robert—G-625 Woold M.
60. G-625 Wyatt W.—G-650 Fandy
61. G-650 Fanney L.—G-653 Rufus
62. G-653 Rufus—G-666 William
63. H-000—H-200 Benjamin G.
64. H-200 Benjamin T.—H-220 James
65. H-220 James—H-252 Kate
66. H-252 Katie—H-320 Sammel
67. H-320 Samuel J.—H-400 Ben
68. H-400 Ben—H-400 Mary
69. H-400 Mary—H-430 T. Frank
70. H-430 T. H.—H-460 Margret
71. H-460 Mark D.—H-522 Carrie
72. H-522 Carrie—H-535 Mary
73. H-535 Mary E.—H-553 John W.
74. H-553 Johnny—H-620 Frank
75. H-620 Frank—H-625 Lily
76. H-625 Linsey—H-632 Sally
77. H-632 Sam—H-652 Charity
78. H-652 Charity—H-665 Vestie
79. I-000—I-656 Homer
80. J-000—J-250 Walter
81. J-250 Walter—J-520 Gyrc Y.
82. J-520 H. Arthur—J-520 Robert
83. J-520 Robert—J-525 David
84. J-525 David—J-525 Mottie
85. J-525 Mottily—J-630 A. L.
86. J-630 Al—J-665 John E.
87. K-000—K-450 John
88. K-450 John—K-523 Henry L.
89. K-523 Henry L.—K-652 Richard
90. K-652 Robert—K-662 Susan
91. L-000—L-135 Mary J.
92. L-135 Matilda—L-200 Ovis
93. L-200 Owen W.—L-250 Richard
94. L-250 Richman I.—L-345 Will
95. L-345 William—L-510 John
96. L-510 John—L-522 William
97. L-522 William—L-600 Maude
98. L-600 Melt—L-663 Jacob
99. M-000—M-200 John E.
100. M-200 John E.—M-223 James C.
101. M-223 John—M-240 John
102. M-240 John—M-245 Mentle
103. M-245 Meta E.—M-252 H. P.
104. M-252 Hal—M-256 Clarence
105. M-256 Clark—M-320 Bert
106. M-320 Berta—M-330 William, Sr.
107. M-331 Arthur—M-435 Docia
108. M-435 Doctor—M-463 Kenni
109. M-463 Jessie T.—M-550 Barney
110. M-550 Benj.—M-600 John
111. M-600 John—M-620 Abenezer
112. M-620 Abeneazer—M-625 Emma
113. M-625 Emma—M-635 Jos. W. H.

114.	M-635 Joseph—M-663 W. Willis
115.	N-000—N-350 John
116.	N-350 John—N-620 Missouri
117.	N-620 Mollie—N-663 Samuel
118.	O-000—O-453 Alfred
119.	O-453 Daniel—O-665 Milton
120.	P-000—P-230 Jesse J.
121.	P-230 Jesse P.—P-355 Cas
122.	P-355 Casley—P-400 Hiram T.
123.	P-400 Holstead—P-420 Pearlie
124.	P-420 Phoade—P-536 Rihard J.
125.	P-536 Richard J.—P-620 Charlie
126.	P-620 Charlie—P-624 Frank
127.	P-624 Frank—P-626 Robert A.
128.	P-626 Robert A.—P-665 Sarah
129.	Q-000—Q-665 Sibble
130.	R-000—R-152 David
131.	R-152 David—R-163 Lillian
132.	R-163 Lillian—R-200 Sarah
133.	R-200 Sarah—R-260 Arthur
134.	R-260 Ashley—R-300 Mary C.
135.	R-300 Mary D.—R-355 Jane
136.	R-355 Jerry A.—R-520 Russell
137.	R-520 Ruth—R-660 John O.
138.	S-000—S-152 Eugene
139.	S-152 Eva—S-165 Guston
140.	S-165 Harvey—S-300 Glenn G.
141.	S-300 Gorege F.—S-320 Samuel
142.	S-320 Samuel E.—S-345 Nepolin
143.	S-345 Newton—S-360 William N.
144.	S-360 William N.—S-364 Maggie
145.	S-364 Maggie—S-435 Andrew
146.	S-435 Andy—S-512 Henry T.
147.	S-512 Henry W.—S-530 Callie
148.	S-530 Callie—S-530 John
149.	S-530 John—S-530 Thomas
150.	S-530 Thomas—S-540 Emma
151.	S-540 Emma L.—S-600 John B.
152.	S-600 John C.—S-655 Jessie
153.	S-655 Joe—S-665 Jasper
154.	T-000—T-300 Sue
155.	T-300 Susan—T-460 Ira
156.	T-460 Ira—T-512 Jessie
157.	T-512 Jessie—T-520 William
158.	T-520 William—T-634 Ellis C.
159.	T-634 Elsie—T-665 Samuel K.
160.	U-000—U-656 Huler
161.	V-000—V-660 David H.
162.	W-000—W-231 Silley J.
163.	W-231 Silvey—W-300 Fly W.
164.	W-300 Ford—W-314 Claud
165.	W-314 Claude—W-325 Zachrie
166.	W-325 Zack—W-360 Marcillen
167.	W-360 Martha E.—W-420 Ambrose
168.	W-420 Ambrose, Jr.—W-425 Betsey
169.	W-426 Betsey E.—W-426 Berton
170.	W-426 Bessie—W-450 George
171.	W-450 George—W-452 Hattie
172.	W-452 Hattie—W-452 Samson
173.	W-452 Samual—W-523 Numa
174.	W-523 Numie—W-630 John F.
175.	W-630 John F.—W-663 James
176.	X-120 John H.—X-640 Marshall Mc
177.	Y-000 Abram—Y-662 Alice M.
178.	Z-000 Dorothea W.—Z-656 Lela A.

OHIO   T1272 (Miracode)

1.	A-000 Agva A.—A-200 Ruth
2.	A-200 Ruth—A-260 Charly
3.	A-260 Chelsea—A-352 Cyntha
4.	A-352 Cynthia R.—A-416 Fred O.
5.	A-416 Fred Theo—A-430 Schooley D.
6.	A-430 Scott—A-452 James H.
7.	A-452 Joe—A-534 Henry
8.	A-534 Henry—A-536 Lewis
9.	A-536 Lewis—A-625 Gustav
10.	A-625 H. Austin—A-653 Margerite
11.	A-653 Maria M.—A-665 Jay R.
12.	B-000—B-200 Abraham
13.	B-200 Abraham—B-200 John A.
14.	B-200 John—B-210 Venia
15.	B-210 Vernon W.—B-236 C. M., Mrs.
16.	B-236 Cail J.—B-246 John
17.	B-246 John—B-255 Lester

18.	B-255 Lester—B-260 Henez
19.	B-260 Henretta—B-262 George
20.	B-262 George—B-300 Thomas E.
21.	B-300 Thomas E.—B-326 Mirtle
22.	B-326 Mollie—B-355 Stanley R.
23.	B-355 Stella—B-400 George
24.	B-400 George—B-400 William G.
25.	B-400 William G.—B-420 Mary
26.	B-420 Mary—B-426 George W.
27.	B-426 George W.—B-450 Edward
28.	B-450 Edward—B-455 Frank W.
29.	B-455 Frank W.—B-500 J. Thomas
30.	B-500 J. W.—B-520 Richard
31.	B-520 Richard T.—B-530 Elbra F.
32.	B-530 Elden J.—B-536 Joseph
33.	B-536 Joseph—B-560 James
34.	B-560 James A.—B-600 Jacob W.
35.	B-600 Jake—B-613 Frank
36.	B-613 Frank—B-620 Fedgo
37.	B-620 Fedor—B-620 Matilda K.
38.	B-620 Matildia—B-622 Sarah S.
39.	B-622 Sarrah—B-625 Edward
40.	B-625 Edward—B-626 John
41.	B-626 John—B-630 John S.
42.	B-630 John S.—B-632 Paul
43.	B-632 Paul—B-635 Jessie
44.	B-635 Jessie—B-645 Ellen C.
45.	B-645 Elmer—B-650 Frank
46.	B-650 Frank—B-650 Malica
47.	B-650 Malinda—B-652 Abraham
48.	B-652 Abraham—B-652 Lizzie
49.	B-652 Lizzie—B-653 John
50.	B-653 John—B-655 William
51.	B-655 William—B-666 Norman A.
52.	C-000—C-145 George
53.	C-145 George—C-160 May
54.	C-160 May—C-200 Henry
55.	C-200 Henry—C-216 John A.
56.	C-216 John C.—C-250 Dave
57.	C-250 David—C-320 Russel
58.	C-320 Ruth E.—C-400 George
59.	C-400 George—C-415 Manuel
60.	C-415 Margaret—C-425 Siuseppe
61.	C-425 Sophia—C-450 John
62.	C-450 John—C-455 Callie
63.	C-455 Calvin O.—C-462 Dennis
64.	C-462 Dennis—C-500 Adison
65.	C-500 Adjuda—C-512 Harry
66.	C-512 Harry C.—C-516 Ella
67.	C-516 Ella—C-534 Benjamen H.
68.	C-534 Ben H.—C-552 Harry
69.	C-552 Harry—C-600 A. T.
70.	C-600 Aaron—C-612 Robert B.
71.	C-612 Robert H., Jr.—C-616 Laura
72.	C-616 Laura—C-621 Beryl
73.	C-621 Betsey—C-625 Joshua
74.	C-625 Josiah—C-635 Homer W.
75.	C-635 Horace G.—C-650 John
76.	C-650 John—C-650 Loretta M.
77.	C-650 Lottie—C-655 Rose C.
78.	C-655 Rose D.—C-666 Flora
79.	D-000 A.—D-120 Bertha M.
80.	D-120 Berty—D-120 Lawrence
81.	D-120 Lawrence—D-132 G. R.
82.	D-132 Gabriel—D-160 Lyman
83.	D-160 M. Z.—D-220 Charlotte W.
84.	D-220 Charls—D-250 Jacob
85.	D-250 Jacob—D-260 William B.
86.	D-260 William B.—D-320 Oliver A.
87.	D-320 Oliver F.—D-400 Charles
88.	D-400 Charles—D-420 John
89.	D-420 John—D-455 Mary
90.	D-455 Mary—D-500 Samuel
91.	D-500 Samuel—D-520 Robert
92.	D-520 Robert—D-540 Amos
93.	D-540 Anastastia—D-552 Faye
94.	D-552 Florence M.—D-600 S. P.
95.	D-600 Sabaria—D-623 Henry
96.	D-623 Henry—D-651 Florentine
97.	D-651 Flornce B.—D-666 Jno. J.
98.	E-000—E-152 Samuel
99.	E-152 Samuel B.—E-231 Frank
100.	E-231 Frank—E-255 L. G.
101.	E-255 Lafe—E-356 Irene
102.	E-356 Isabel—E-422 Phillip
103.	E-422 R. A.—E-513 Henry L.
104.	E-513 James A.—E-550 Frank

105.	E-550 Frank—E-650 John N.
106.	E-650 John W.—E-665 Vincent
107.	F-000 A. C.—F-200 Mary
108.	F-200 Mary—F-236 Tilden J.
109.	F-236 Tobias—F-260 James D.
110.	F-260 James E.—F-325 Sarah
111.	F-325 Sarah—F-420 Frederick
112.	F-420 Frederick—F-432 Edwin W.
113.	F-432 Effie—F-455 Charles L.
114.	F-455 Charles L.—F-463 Mart
115.	F-463 Martaret—F-534 Howard G.
116.	F-534 Isaac—F-600 Nicholas
117.	F-600 Nicholas—F-622 Alice
118.	F-622 Alice—F-626 James
119.	F-626 James—F-635 Frank A.
120.	F-635 Frank C.—F-651 Joseph B.
121.	F-651 Judson R.—F-652 Tilley
122.	F-652 Tillie—F-666 Walter T.
123.	G-000 Adam—G-150 Thomas
124.	G-150 Thomas—G-230 Henry
125.	G-230 Henry—G-300 Charles
126.	G-300 Charles—G-350 Earl
127.	G-350 Earl H.—G-400 Mary
128.	G-400 Mary—G-421 Bessie
129.	G-421 Blaine—G-431 Hannah
130.	G-431 Harris—G-455 NR
131.	G-455 Ollie—G-523 Martin
132.	G-523 Mary—G-600 Dorothy
133.	G-600 Dorsey D.—G-610 Yacob
134.	G-610 Yerni—G-615 William
135.	G-615 William—G-620 Luther B.
136.	G-620 Luther F.—G-625 Thomas
137.	G-625 Thomas—G-635 Emma
138.	G-635 Emma—G-650 Berdie
139.	G-650 Bernhard—G-650 Roy E.
140.	G-650 Roy G.—G-653 Mary
141.	G-653 Mary—G-666 Robert
142.	H-000 A. F.—H-125 Louis
143.	H-125 Louis D.—H-155 Fred H.
144.	H-155 Fred J.—H-160 John
145.	H-160 John—H-200 Charles B.
146.	H-200 Charles B.—H-200 John M.
147.	H-200 John M.—H-220 Alfred
148.	H-220 Alfred F.—H-235 Frances
149.	H-235 Frances—H-246 Alwin J.
150.	H-246 Amanda—H-252 Mary C.
151.	H-252 Mary D.—H-262 Samuel P.
152.	H-262 Simon C.—H-314 James
153.	H-314 James F.—H-325 Margaret A.
154.	H-325 Margaret L.—H-364 Jacob
155.	H-364 James—H-400 Hanna S.
156.	H-400 Hannah—H-400 Roscoe D.
157.	H-400 Rose—H-420 Louis
158.	H-420 Louis—H-432 John
159.	H-432 John—H-452 William
160.	H-452 William—H-500 Denny
161.	H-500 Denny W.—H-516 Howard
162.	H-516 Howard—H-520 Russell E.
163.	H-520 Russell—H-526 Henry C.
164.	H-526 Henry H.—H-536 Florence
165.	H-536 Florence A.—H-543 Helen W.
166.	H-543 Hellen—H-553 Margret
167.	H-553 Margurite F.—H-600 Flora
168.	H-600 Flora E.—H-616 Margarett
169.	H-616 Margeret—H-620 Ruth
170.	H-620 Ruth—H-626 Eldon
171.	H-626 Elizabeth—H-630 William
172.	H-630 William—H-635 Julius W.
173.	H-635 Julius W., Sr.—H-650 Mike
174.	H-650 Mike—H-656 Arthur
175.	H-656 Arthur—H-665 Velma
176.	I-000 Charles—I-540 Levi
177.	I-540 Levi—I-665 Willie G.
178.	J-000—J-212 John C.
179.	J-212 John C.—J-250 Samuel
180.	J-250 Samuel—J-520 Albert
181.	J-520 Albert—J-520 Hazel
182.	J-520 Hazel M.—J-520 Roruch D.
183.	J-520 Rosa—J-525 Asa P.
184.	J-525 Asa R.—J-525 James A.
185.	J-525 James B.—J-525 Warren, Sr.
186.	J-525 Wasalie—J-650 Joseph
187.	J-650 Joseph—J-655 Lillian
188.	K-000 A. H.—K-146 James
189.	K-146 James—K-200 Helia
190.	K-200 Henrietta—K-236 John
191.	K-236 John—K-260 Daniel A.

192.	K-260 Daniel B.—K-325 Rory
193.	K-325 Rose B.—K-400 Jacob
194.	K-400 Jacob—K-420 Anna M.
195.	K-420 Anna M.—K-450 Floria
196.	K-450 Flosin—K-456 John G.
197.	K-456 John H.—K-500 Frank
198.	K-500 Frank—K-513 Chas. F.
199.	K-513 Christian—K-520 James
200.	K-520 James—K-523 Wm.
201.	K-523 Wm. D.—K-532 Bessie
202.	K-532 Bessie C.—K-552 Frederick
203.	K-552 Frieda—K-613 Carrie
204.	K-613 Carrie—K-621 Joe
205.	K-621 Joe—K-632 Anton
206.	K-632 Anton—K-652 Horoce O.
207.	K-652 Hosea—K-666 Emile
208.	L-000—L-100 John
209.	L-100 John—L-146 August
210.	L-146 August—L-165 William
211.	L-165 William—L-200 Joes
212.	L-200 Johann—L-216 John
213.	L-216 John—L-236 William
214.	L-236 William—L-260 Frank
215.	L-260 Frank—L-320 Evaline B.
216.	L-320 Everett—L-350 Thomas
217.	L-350 Thomas—L-500 Albert B.
218.	L-500 Albert B.—L-516 Eugene
219.	L-516 Eva—L-520 Jeremiah
220.	L-520 Jeremiah—L-523 John L.
221.	L-523 John M.—L-532 Leon
222.	L-532 Leon—L-550 Lila
223.	L-550 Lillian—L-600 Fred I.
224.	L-600 Fred J.—L-652 George
225.	L-652 George—L-666 Rachel
226.	M-000 A. G.—M-200 Chas.
227.	M-200 Chas.—M-200 Mary
228.	M-200 Mary—M-213 Sam
229.	M-213 Sam—M-220 Michael
230.	M-220 Michael—M-235 Henry
231.	M-235 Henry—M-240 Grover
232.	M-240 Grover—M-242 John
233.	M-242 John—M-245 Joseph C.
234.	M-245 Joseph C.—M-250 Frances M.
235.	M-250 Frances M.—M-252 Dallas J.
236.	M-252 Dalril—M-254 Elisabeth
237.	M-254 Elisabeth—M-256 Edna
238.	M-256 Edna P.—M-260 Sameul
239.	M-260 Samial—M-263 Theodore
240.	M-263 Theodore J.—M-320 Bertha
241.	M-320 Bertha—M-324 George W.
242.	M-324 Gerogie—M-350 Frank
243.	M-350 Frank—M-400 Wm. C.
244.	M-400 Wm. Charles—M-425 James R.
245.	M-425 James R. J.—M-450 Robert
246.	M-450 Robert—M-460 Charles J.
247.	M-460 Charles J.—M-460 Harry
248.	M-460 Harry—M-460 Louisa
249.	M-460 Louisa—M-460 William
250.	M-460 William—M-500 Vanguda
251.	M-500 Vasile—M-525 Carmino
252.	M-525 Caroline—M-535 William
253.	M-535 William—M-600 Alden D.
254.	M-600 Aleax—M-600 George W.
255.	M-600 George W.—M-600 Mattie
256.	M-600 Mattie—M-610 John
257.	M-610 John—M-620 David W.
258.	M-620 David W.—M-620 Joseph
259.	M-620 Joseph—M-621 Moses
260.	M-621 Nicholas—M-625 Ethel
261.	M-625 Ethel D.—M-630 Edward
262.	M-630 Edward—M-635 Godfrey I.
263.	M-635 Goerge M.—M-640 Stephen
264.	M-640 Stephen D.—M-666 Oscar
265.	N-000 A. G.—N-162 Frank L.
266.	N-162 Frank P.—N-240 Geo. L.
267.	N-240 Geo. W.—N-256 Lucia E.
268.	N-256 Mabel—N-400 Harry L.
269.	N-400 Harry R.—N-435 Susan R.
270.	N-435 Susana—N-600 Maria Gertrude
271.	N-600 Marian A.—N-664 William F.
272.	O-000 Amel—O-000 Minnie E.
273.	O-200 Minorott—O-256 Catherine
274.	O-256 Catherine—O-420 Joseph J.
275.	O-420 Julius—O-540 Joseph
276.	O-540 Joseph—O-665 Warren J.

277.	P-000 Aaron C.—P-160 Letita
278.	P-160 Leud—P-220 Peter
279.	P-220 Petrina—P-263 Clara
280.	P-263 Clarence—P-330 William
281.	P-330 William—P-362 Charles E.
282.	P-362 Charles E.—P-366 Carmine
283.	P-366 Danuel—P-412 Daniel
284.	P-412 Daniel—P-421 Clara J.
285.	P-421 Claud W.—P-453 Edna
286.	P-453 Edward—P-512 John H.
287.	P-512 Joseph R.—P-550 Henry
288.	P-550 Ira E.—P-620 Calvin
289.	P-620 Calvin A.—P-620 Richard
290.	P-620 Richard—P-625 Erich
291.	P-625 Erick—P-630 Clarence
292.	P-630 Clarence D.—P-636 William E.
293.	P-636 William E.—P-666 Stephono
294.	Q-000 Alice E.—Q-661 Carl
295.	R-000—R-100 Matilda
296.	R-100 Matilda—R-150 Human
297.	R-150 Hyman—R-160 George A.
298.	R-160 George B.—R-200 Alice C.
299.	R-200 Alice E.—R-200 George
300.	R-200 George—R-200 Mary
301.	R-200 Mary—R-216 Ida M.
302.	R-216 Jacob—R-240 Gus
303.	R-240 Gus D.—R-251 Henry
304.	R-251 Henry—R-260 William
305.	R-260 William—R-263 Rhoda
306.	R-263 Richard—R-300 John D.
307.	R-300 John D.—R-320 Elizabeth
308.	R-320 Elizabeth—R-330 George H.
309.	R-330 George W.—R-360 Carey
310.	R-360 Carey—R-400 John L.
311.	R-400 John M.—R-500 Augusta, Mrs.
312.	R-500 Augustus L.—R-520 Alfred
313.	R-520 Alfred J.—R-526 Etta
314.	R-526 Everett—R-550 Clay C.
315.	R-550 Clay M.—R-620 Fred
316.	R-620 Fred—R-665 Wm.
317.	S-000 A.—S-100 John H.
318.	S-100 John H.—S-126 Harley M.
319.	S-126 Harrey F.—S-143 Charles K.
320.	S-143 Charles M.—S-152 Stefe
321.	S-152 Stella—S-160 John
322.	S-160 John—S-162 Wiley T.
323.	S-162 Wilford—S-165 Lucinda
324.	S-165 Lucinda—S-216 Fred
325.	S-216 Fred—S-240 George
326.	S-240 George—S-260 Nellie
327.	S-260 Nellie—S-300 Jessie A.
328.	S-300 Jessie D.—S-314 Edwin W.
329.	S-314 Edwin W.—S-315 Ulissus G.
330.	S-315 Ulysis S.—S-320 Lena T.
331.	S-320 Lenie A.—S-325 Rade
332.	S-325 Ralph—S-335 Robert H.
333.	S-335 Robert W.—S-342 John
334.	S-342 John—S-350 Lizzie
335.	S-350 Lizzie—S-352 Matin
336.	S-352 Matsek—S-356 William
337.	S-356 William—S-362 Daniel
338.	S-362 Daniel—S-363 Elizabeth
339.	S-363 Elizabeth—S-364 Mary C.
340.	S-364 Mary E.—S-400 Frank
341.	S-400 Frank—S-415 Daniel H.
342.	S-415 Daniel H.—S-420 William
343.	S-420 William—S-432 Frank
344.	S-432 Frank—S-450 Marguerite
345.	S-450 Marguerite A.—S-460 Philip
346.	S-460 Philip—S-500 William J.
347.	S-500 William J.—S-520 Andrew
348.	S-520 Andrew—S-524 Charles
349.	S-524 Charles—S-530 Albert L.
350.	S-530 Albert L.—S-530 Edgar
351.	S-530 Edgar—S-530 Harry
352.	S-530 Harry—S-530 Joseph H.
353.	S-530 Joseph H.—S-530 Pious P.
354.	S-530 Pittek—S-532 Catherine
355.	S-532 Catherine—S-536 Clair J.
356.	S-536 Clara—S-536 Margaret
357.	S-536 Margaret—S-543 Clinton M.
358.	S-543 Cuban J.—S-552 Otto
359.	S-552 Otto—S-563 John J.
360.	S-563 John J.—S-610 Tully J.
361.	S-610 Turive—S-620 Valentine

362.	S-620 Valentine H.—S-632 Joseph
363.	S-632 Joseph—S-650 Nellie
364.	S-650 Nellie—S-666 Morris D.
365.	T-000 Abel—T-200 Jesse B.
366.	T-200 Jessie—T-265 Laurence
367.	T-265 Laurence—T-400 Amalei
368.	T-400 Amanda—T-460 Cleo P.
369.	T-460 Cleon—T-500 Benjamin
370.	T-500 Benjamin F.—T-512 Mariah
371.	T-512 Marie—T-520 George W.
372.	T-520 George W.—T-525 Jacob A.
373.	T-525 James—T-610 Bessie
374.	T-610 Bessie L.—T-623 Allen S.
375.	T-623 Allison D.—T-650 Harry A.
376.	T-650 Harry B.—T-656 Katie K.
377.	T-656 Kinsey F.—T-666 Samuel W.
378.	U-000 Atyil—U-600 Peter
379.	U-600 Robert—U-660 William L.
380.	V-000 Adelbert—V-262 Jessie K.
381.	V-262 John—V-460 Fred
382.	V-460 Fred C.—V-526 Ectelle
383.	V-526 Edgar C.—V-620 Ferentsz
384.	V-620 Ferentz—V-663 Vanzel
385.	W-000 Abe—W-160 Henry S.
386.	W-160 Henry S.—W-200 Lawrence
387.	W-200 Lawrence—W-231 Essig N.
388.	W-231 Ethal—W-252 Anna
389.	W-252 Anna—W-256 Joseph, Jr.
390.	W-256 Joseph K.—W-300 Esta
391.	W-300 Esta—W-300 Selden
392.	W-300 Selwin—W-324 Lena
393.	W-324 Lena—W-340 William M.
394.	W-340 William N.—W-360 Wm. B.
395.	W-360 Wm. B.—W-400 John H.
396.	W-400 John H.—W-414 John G.
397.	W-414 John G.—W-420 Helen
398.	W-420 Helen—W-420 William H.
399.	W-420 William H.—W-425 George
400.	W-425 George—W-425 William
401.	W-425 William—W-432 Annie
402.	W-432 Anson G.—W-436 William H.
403.	W-436 William I.—W-452 Eva
404.	W-452 Eva—W-452 Reese
405.	W-452 Reese D.—W-462 Wilson H.
406.	W-463 A.—W-526 Adam
407.	W-526 Adda B.—W-552 Alfred B.
408.	W-552 Alice—W-623 Charles
409.	W-623 Charles—W-630 Gus
410.	W-630 Gustav—W-650 Ethel
411.	W-650 Ethel M.—W-665 Losin T.
412.	X-100 Alfred A.—X-656 Lillian
413.	Y-000 Albert J.—Y-520 Belle
414.	Y-520 Belle—Y-526 Benjamin
415.	Y-526 Berdine—Y-663 Paul
416.	Z-000 Adam—Z-400 Ray M.
417.	Z-400 Robert—Z-565 Fred
418.	Z-565 Fred—Z-663 Anna

OKLAHOMA T1273 (Miracode)

1.	A-000—A-341 Werner
2.	A-342 Anthony—A-450 Andrew E.
3.	A-450 Andrew J.—A-536 Leon
4.	A-536 Leonard—A-665 Marie
5.	B-000—B-230 Della
6.	B-230 Denis—B-260 Melvin H.
7.	B-260 Merce—B-350 David A.
8.	B-350 Delah—B-420 Earnest F.
9.	B-420 Earnest M.—B-452 Andrew
10.	B-452 Andrew—B-520 Will
11.	B-520 Will—B-600 Edward
12.	B-600 Edward G.—B-620 Sam
13.	B-620 Sam—B-630 J. M.
14.	B-630 J. O.—B-636 Joseph
15.	B-636 Joseph C.—B-650 Marine
16.	B-650 Marie—B-653 Emma
17.	B-653 Emma—B-666 Joseph M.
18.	C-000—C-165 Robert
19.	C-165—C-235 W. Dee
20.	C-235 W. W.—C-400 Charles
21.	C-400 Charles—C-434 Jerie
22.	C-434 Jerry—C-460 Nanva L.
23.	C-460 Naoma—C-514 James
24.	C-514 James—C-552 John
25.	C-552 John A.—C-616 Marshell
26.	C-616 Mart—C-632 Oggie A.

27. C-632 Oliver—C-650 Robert
28. C-650 Robert—C-665 Tucker
29. D-000—D-120 W. P.
30. D-120 W. P.—D-242 John P.
31. D-242 John S.—D-400 Chraley
32. D-400 Christin—D-520 Eliza D.
33. D-520 Elizabeth—D-600 Lenul P.
34. D-600 Leon—D-663 John
35. E-000—E-325 L. C.
36. E-325 Leroy D.—E-452 Lou
37. E-452 M. M.—E-663 Wilmer
38. F-000—F-400 Evvie
39. F-400 E. S.—F-462 Emmitt
40. F-462 Emmitt—F-624 Marrus
41. F-624 Martha—F-655 Ava O.
42. F-655 Avanor—F-666 William
43. G-000—G-316 Leander
44. G-316 Lissa—G-430 Clersey
45. G-430 Cocket—G-600 David C.
46. G-600 David M.—G-625 Ellis
47. G-625 Elmer L.—G-650 Jacob
48. G-650 Jacob—G-665 Horrace
49. H-000—H-200 Dean
50. H-200 Deitmer—H-235 Lillie
51. H-235 Lizzie—H-300 Emory W.
52. H-300 Emry—H-362 Frank E.
53. H-362 Frank M.—H-400 Wesley
54. H-400 Wesley—H-453 Lither
55. H-453 Liza—H-524 J. T.
56. H-524 Jacob—H-542 Bert A.
57. H-542 Eliha—H-620 Albert
58. H-620 Albert—H-630 Fred
59. H-630 Fred—H-651 Joe
60. H-651 John—H-665 Henry
61. I-000—I-660 Lincise W.
62. J-000—J-420 Howard
63. J-420 Isabelle—J-520 Marshal
64. J-520 Marshal T.—J-525 Gertie
65. J-525 Gertrude—J-612 JA
66. J-612 James—J-665 Willia
67. K-000—K-400 Okla
68. K-400 Oliver—K-520 John
69. K-520 John—K-620 Cirrol Z.
70. K-620 Charley—K-662 Karl
71. L-000—L-200 Alfred
72. L-200 Alfred—L-240 W. A.
73. L-240 W. D.—L-400 A. B.
74. L-400 A. W.—L-520 William
75. L-520 William—L-613 Ajckson
76. L-614 Benla—L-665 B. J.
77. M-000—M-200 Salbie J.
78. M-200 Sallie—M-235 M. H.
79. M-235 M. P.—M-245 William
80. M-245 William—M-254 Clara
81. M-254 Clarence—M-265 Edward
82. M-265 Elijah—M-342 Nellie M.
83. M-342 Newt—M-456 Tom
84. M-456 William—M-520 Charles L.
85. M-520 Charles M.—M-600 Festus L.
86. M-600 Ffed—M-620 Eligah
87. M-620 Elijah A.—M-625 Thomas M.
88. M-625 Thomas M.—M-650 N. R.
89. M-650 Namel—M-666 Robt.
90. N-000—N-350 Sebastian
91. N-350 Sherman—N-630 Ollie
92. N-630 Perry W.—N-665 Peter
93. O-000—O-520 Elbert
94. O-520 Elija—O-662 May
95. P-000—P-300 William
96. P-300 William—P-400 Geroge
97. P-400 Geroge—P-460 Clints
98. P-460 Curti—P-620 Charles W.
99. P-620 Charley—P-626 Arthur
100. P-626 Arthur C.—P-660 William
101. P-660 William—P-666 Nepolion
102. Q-000 Hg Ah—Q-654 Ha
103. R-000—R-153 Liddie C.
104. R-153 Louis B.—R-200 James
105. R-200 James A.—R-250 Nely
106. R-250 Nora—R-300 James A.
107. R-300 James A.—R-361 Isaac J.
108. R-361 J.—R-525 Lewis
109. R-525 Lillian B.—R-663 Thomas
110. S-000—S-160 Henry
111. S-160 Henry—S-250 Carolone
112. S-250 Charles—S-315 Joe
113. S-315 Joe—S-340 Samuel

114. S-340 Samuel—S-360 Philip
115. S-360 Philip—S-400 John
116. S-400 John—S-452 Robt. W.
117. S-452 Rom—S-524 William
118. S-524 William A.—S-530 Jesse W.
119. S-530 Jesse W. S.—S-532 Santos
120. S-532 Sarah J.—S-560 Lafayette G.
121. S-560 Laman—S-640 S.
122. S-640 S. B.—S-665 Wanson
123. T-000—T-360 William
124. T-360 William—T-500 Kera
125. T-500 L. M.—T-520 Perl
126. T-520 Perran—T-626 Andrew W.
127. T-626 Arlander—T-665 Lizzie
128. U-000—U-656 Jose
129. V-000—V-600 John
130. V-600 Landram—V-664 G. W.
131. W-000—W-241 J. J.
132. W-241 J. N.—W-300 Louis
133. W-300 Louis—W-325 William W.
134. W-325 William W.—W-400 William S.
135. W-400 William S.—W-422 W. T.
136. W-422 W. W.—W-426 I. W.
137. W-426 I. A.—W-452 Croel S.
138. W-452 Cryhus—W-456 Grant
139. W-456 Hattie B.—W-623 George
140. W-623 George—W-665 Mary
141. X-160 James—X-620 George H.
142. Y-000—Y-662 N. R.
143. Z-000—Z-662 Frnk

PENNSYLVANIA   T1274 (Miracode)
See rolls 529–688 for Philadelphia County.

1.   A-000 Adam—A-200 Clara L.
2.   A-200 Clarence—A-250 Alfonso
3.   A-250 Ali—A-325 Sadie F.
4.   A-325 Sallie M.—A-352 Stella M.
5.   A-352 Stephani—A-416 William
6.   A-416 William—A-432 Kelso
7.   A-432 Keneth E.—A-452 Albert J.
8.   A-452 Alegi—A-524 Penm
9.   A-524 Percy—A-536 Charlie J.
10. A-536 Charlie R.—A-536 Oscar
11. A-536 Oscar—A-620 J. D.
12. A-620 J. D.—A-652 Mary
13. A-652 Mary—A-665 Mike
14. B-000 A. J.—B-152 John J.
15. B-152 John M.—B-200 Felix Jun
16. B-200 Felix Jun—B-200 Micheal
17. B-200 Micheal—B-220 Catherine
18. B-220 Caveransi—B-234 Grace C.
19. B-234 Gustave—B-240 Patrick E.
20. B-240 Patrick H.—B-252 Bernard
21. B-252 Bernard—B-260 Annie
22. B-260 Annie—B-260 John Y.
23. B-260 John Y.—B-263 Julia
24. B-263 K. A.—B-300 William
25. B-300 William—B-326 Amelia
26. B-326 Anderio—B-350 John
27. B-350 John—B-362 Peter
28. B-362 Peter—B-400 James M.
29. B-400 James M.—B-410 Mike
30. B-410 Mike—B-420 John
31. B-420 John—B-422 Julian
32. B-422 Julian—B-430 Samuel
33. B-430 Samuel—B-450 John
34. B-450 John—B-455 Joseph
35. B-455 Joseph—B-500 Fackenthall
36. B-500 Fannie—B-516 John H.
37. B-516 John H.—B-524 Ruth A.
38. B-524 Sallie C.—B-530 James
39. B-530 James—B-536 Joseph
40. B-536 Joseph—B-560 Carl B.
41. B-560 Carl R.—B-600 Elizabeth M.
42. B-600 Elizabeth M.—B-600 Marian E.
43. B-600 Marice—B-612 S. Augusta
44. B-612 S. Charles—B-620 Edward
45. B-620 Edward—B-620 Josep
46. B-620 Joseph—B-620 Violet A.
47. B-620 Violet D.—B-623 Emil
48. B-623 Emil—B-625 Alriey
49. B-625 Alva O.—B-626 Florence
50. B-626 Florence—B-630 Frank
51. B-630 Frank A.—B-631 Fredrick

52. B-631 Fredrick W.—B-634 Edward
53. B-634 Edward—B-635 Lizzie
54. B-635 Lizzie M.—B-643 Chuck W.
55. B-643 Clara O.—B-650 Elizabeth
56. B-650 Elizabeth—B-650 John E.
57. B-650 John E. M.—B-650 Smichael
58. B-650 Smiley—B-652 Frances
59. B-652 Frances—B-652 Susan
60. B-652 Susan—B-653 Susan
61. B-653 Susan A.—B-656 Catharine
62. B-656 Catherine—B-666 Sarah
63. C-000 Adam—C-140 Charles A.
64. C-140 Charles A.—C-155 Theodore A.
65. C-155 Thoams—C-200 Antonio
66. C-200 Antonio—C-200 Mike
67. C-200 Mike—C-230 Rasse
68. C-230 Ray L.—C-245 Frnk
69. C-245 Gaetano—C-265 Emanuel
70. C-265 Emma—C-352 George
71. C-352 George—C-400 Mary H.
72. C-400 Mary I.—C-416 Isibell C.
73. C-416 Isoda—C-425 John
74. C-425 John—C-436 William
75. C-436 William—C-452 Jame
76. C-452 James—C-455 William
77. C-455 William—C-462 John O.
78. C-462 John P.—C-500 John
79. C-500 John—C-514 Elizabeth
80. C-514 Elizabeth—C-516 Edwin
81. C-516 Edwin—C-526 Crist
82. C-526 Crist—C-540 Tony
83. C-540 Tony—C-560 Anna
84. C-560 Anna—C-600 Bessy
85. C-600 Bettie—C-610 George
86. C-610 George—C-616 Bertha
87. C-616 Bertha A.—C-620 John
88. C-620 John—C-623 J. Darret, Jr.
89. C-623 J. Harry—C-625 Julia B.
90. C-625 Julias—C-634 Katharine
91. C-634 Katherine—C-640 Elmer H.
92. C-640 Elmer H.—C-642 Oscar
93. C-642 Oscar—C-651 William G.
94. C-651 William H.—C-655 William B.
95. C-655 William C.—C-666 Sara
96. D-000 Clare—D-120 Booker
97. D-120 Borden L.—D-120 John T.
98. D-120 John T.—D-125 Edith
99. D-125 Edith—D-146 Francis
100. D-146 Francis M.—D-162 Michel
101. D-162 Mike—D-200 William J.
102. D-200 William J.—D-246 Mary T.
103. D-246 Melton—D-252 Pawel
104. D-252 Payson K.—D-263 Jane
105. D-263 Jane—D-320 Mary
106. D-320 Mary A.—D-362 David B.
107. D-362 David B.—D-400 John P.
108. D-400 John P.—D-421 Elizabeth
109. D-421 Frank B.—D-452 Irvin
110. D-452 Irvin—D-500 James W.
111. D-500 James W.—D-515 Richard E.
112. D-515 Richard H.—D-522 Mike
113. D-522 Mike—D-532 Mary E.
114. D-532 Mathew—D-543 John W.
115. D-543 John W.—D-560 Mildred
116. D-560 Millie—D-612 Lewis
117. D-612 Lewis—D-622 John
118. D-622 John—D-645 Hettie E.
119. D-645 Hillborn—D-666 Joseph
120. E-000 Andrew—E-152 Joseph
121. E-152 Joseph—E-164 Robert
122. E-164 Robert—E-240 John
123. E-240 John—E-256 Louisa
124. E-256 Louisa C.—E-352 Eleth
125. E-352 Elias—E-420 Charles R.
126. E-420 Charles R.—E-450 William A.
127. E-450 William J.—E-524 John
128. E-524 John—E-600 B. Frank
129. E-600 Barbara—E-652 Lawrence
130. E-652 Lenora E.—E-665 John
131. F-000 A. Grant—F-200 James C.
132. F-200 James D.—F-230 Samuel
133. F-230 Samuel A.—F-250 Robert
134. F-250 Robert—F-260 Peter
135. F-260 Peter—F-326 Rosa
136. F-326 Rosa E.—F-412 Frederick
137. F-412 Furiois—F-425 J. Staley

138.	F-425 J. William—F-435 Iraase
139.	F-435 Irvin—F-455 Rachel
140.	F-455 Rachel—F-500 Edward
141.	F-500 Edward—F-525 Patrick
142.	F-525 Patrick—F-600 Elmer
143.	F-600 Elmer—F-612 Sylvia
144.	F-612 T. J.—F-622 Julia
145.	F-622 Julia—F-630 Alsaudro
146.	F-630 Alton H.—F-632 Vergie
147.	F-632 Vernal G.—F-640 Susan R.
148.	F-640 Susannah E.—F-652 Geo. W., Jr.
149.	F-652 George—F-653 Jennie S.
150.	F-653 Jeremiah—F-666 William
151.	G-000 A. Erwin—G-140 George
152.	G-140 George A.—G-200 Annie
153.	G-200 Annie—G-230 William H.
154.	G-230 William H.—G-256 Stella
155.	G-256 Stephen—G-320 Daisy
156.	G-320 Daisy M.—G-350 John B.
157.	G-350 John C.—G-400
158.	G-400 Martha—G-420 George
159.	G-420 George—G-426 August
160.	G-426 August—G-432 Alexander
161.	G-432 Alexander—G-452 Lawrazo
162.	G-452 Lawrell M.—G-514 Philip
163.	G-514 Phillip P.—G-534 James
164.	G-534 James B.—G-600 Ercher
165.	G-600 Ernest—G-610 Henry
166.	G-610 Henry A.—G-613 John H.
167.	G-613 John H.—G-616 John Y.
168.	G-616 Johnson—G-620 John A.
169.	G-620 John A.—G-623 John
170.	G-623 John—G-630 George
171.	G-630 George—G-635 John A.
172.	G-635 John A.—G-650 Charles
173.	G-650 Charles—G-650 Rachael
174.	G-650 Racheal—G-653 David
175.	G-653 David—G-656 Emanuel G.
176.	G-656 Emanuel H.—G-666 William MB
177.	H-000 A. D.—H-122 Dominic
178.	H-122 Ella M.—H-150 Martin
179.	H-150 Martin H.—H-155 Sadie J.
180.	H-155 Sadie J.—H-160 Louis C.
181.	H-160 Louis E.—H-200 Arba W.
182.	H-200 Arbison C.—H-200 Hatton
183.	H-200 Havey H.—H-200 Milton
184.	H-200 Milton H.—H-220 Edith
185.	H-220 Edith A.—H-233 Jacob
186.	H-233 Jacob—H-243 Marguarite
187.	H-243 Marguret E.—H-252 David H.
188.	H-252 David J.—H-260 Frank
189.	H-260 Frank—H-300 Homer H.
190.	H-300 Horace—H-322 Maria
191.	H-322 Mariah—H-352 Anna
192.	H-352 Anna G.—H-400 Edward H.
193.	H-400 Edward J.—H-400 Mary A.
194.	H-400 Mary A.—H-416 Laura
195.	H-416 Lawrence—H-430 Fred
196.	H-430 Fred—H-450 Milton C.
197.	H-450 Milton H.—H-455 Jurdon A.
198.	H-455 Kate—H-500 Fred D.
199.	H-500 Fred E.—H-515 Albert
200.	H-515 Charles K.—H-520 Michael J.
201.	H-520 Michael J.—H-525 Ellen
202.	H-525 Ellen—H-535 Elwin
203.	H-535 Emily—H-540 Alberte
204.	H-540 Alcinda—H-546 Louis
205.	H-546 Louis W.—H-560 Goerg E.
206.	H-560 Goerge—H-600 Hrney R.
207.	H-600 Hugh—H-615 Clara
208.	H-615 Clara L.—H-620 Julia
209.	H-620 Julia—H-625 George W.
210.	H-625 George W.—H-630 Luther R.
211.	H-630 Luther W.—H-635 Allen R.
212.	H-635 Allen S.—H-640 Blanche
213.	H-640 Blanche—H-652 Daniel S.
214.	H-652 Daniel T.—H-656 Fred
215.	H-656 Fred—H-666 Sadie
216.	I-000 Charles R.—I-520 Lizzie M.
217.	I-520 Lonnie—I-665 John
218.	J-000 A. B.—J-210 Miacheal
219.	J-210 Michael—J-250 Harry
220.	J-250 Harry—J-452 Daniel
221.	J-452 F. M.—J-520 Eler T.
222.	J-520 Eli—J-520 Kate

223.	J-520 Kate—J-520 William
224.	J-520 William—J-525 Aurt
225.	J-525 Aurtha—J-525 James H.
226.	J-525 James H.—J-525 Walter
227.	J-525 Walter—J-635 Leroy
228.	J-635 Lewis H.—J-665 Tona
229.	K-000 Abye—K-132 Martin
230.	K-132 Martin—K-155 Louis
231.	K-155 Louis—K-200 Derwin C.
232.	K-200 Derwin C.—K-216 Jurex
233.	K-216 Katherine—K-240 Earl
234.	K-240 Earl C.—K-252 Mary
235.	K-252 Mary—K-300 Ella M.
236.	K-300 Ellan—K-342 Nicholas
237.	K-342 Nicholas—K-400 Harry
238.	K-400 Harry—K-410 Abrams S.
239.	K-410 Adah—K-420 Mary
240.	K-420 Mary—K-450 Catherine
241.	K-450 Catherine—K-452 Charles
242.	K-452 Charles—K-460 Edward
243.	K-460 Edward—K-500 Cyrus
244.	K-500 Cyrus F.—K-510 Charles E.
245.	K-510 Charles F.—K-520 Charles W.
246.	K-520 Charles W.—K-520 Paul
247.	K-520 Paul—K-524 Reuben
248.	K-524 Reuben B.—K-532 Carl
249.	K-532 Carl—K-550 Catherine
250.	K-550 Catherine—K-600 Eliza B., Mrs.
251.	K-600 Elizabeth—K-615 John
252.	K-615 John—K-620 William
253.	K-620 William—K-625 Stephen
254.	K-625 Stephen—K-636 Elizabeth
255.	K-636 Elizabeth—K-652 Anthony
256.	K-652 Anthony—K-660 Mercedes
257.	K-660 Michael—K-666 Mary
258.	L-000 A. C.—L-100 George R.
259.	L-100 George S.—L-125 Paya
260.	L-125 Peter—L-152 Arch
261.	L-152 Archibald—L-163 Kathryn E.
262.	L-163 Katie—L-200 George
263.	L-200 George—L-200 Melo
264.	L-200 Melton—L-220 Florence L.
265.	L-220 Florence M.—L-234 Sylvester M.
266.	L-234 Thomas—L-250 Paul
267.	L-250 Paul—L-260 Raymond
268.	L-260 Raymond A.—L-320 Andrew
269.	L-320 Andrew—L-326 John
270.	L-326 John—L-360 Margaret
271.	L-360 Margaret—L-500 Emanuel
272.	L-500 Emanuel—L-516 Josephine E.
273.	L-516 Joshua P.—L-520 James
274.	L-520 James—L-520 William
275.	L-520 William—L-526 Jared
276.	L-526 Jared—L-532 Theodore
277.	L-532 Theodore—L-550 Phillip
278.	L-550 Phoebie—L-600 Frank
279.	L-600 Frank—L-626 Omas
280.	L-626 Peter—L-666 Nathan K.
281.	M-000 A. F.—M-200 Arm
282.	M-200 Arminta—M-200 John
283.	M-200 John—M-200 Veto
284.	M-200 Vickovic—M-214 Nellie
285.	M-214 Ohrve M.—M-220 Frank
286.	M-220 Frank—M-230 Charles
287.	M-230 Charles—M-235 Edward
288.	M-235 Edward—M-236 Steve
289.	M-236 Steven—M-240 Metro
290.	M-240 Metro—M-242 Frank
291.	M-242 Frank—M-243 Frank
292.	M-243 Frank—M-245 Lydia A.
293.	M-245 Lydia G.—M-250 Baltley
294.	M-250 Baptist—M-250 Mittie
295.	M-250 Moch—M-252 John
296.	M-252 John—M-253 William H.
297.	M-253 William H.—M-254 William Mck.
298.	M-254 William N.—M-256 W. P.
299.	M-256 W. R.—M-260 Mary
300.	M-260 Mary—M-262 William
301.	M-262 William—M-265 Ashauer
302.	M-265 Augustine—M-300 Valocchi
303.	M-300 Vance R.—M-320 Theodore P.
304.	M-320 Theodore S.—M-325 Ann
305.	M-325 Anna—M-352 John

306.	M-352 John—M-400 John
307.	M-400 John—M-420 John
308.	M-420 John—M-430 Edward
309.	M-430 Edward—M-450 Norman
310.	M-450 O. P.—M-460 Augustus
311.	M-460 Augustus—M-460 Eugene
312.	M-460 Eugene—M-460 Jacob A.
313.	M-460 Jacob A.—M-460 Maria
314.	M-460 Maria—M-460 Thomas R.
315.	M-460 Thomas S.—M-500 Jacob R.
316.	M-500 Jacob R.—M-520 George D.
317.	M-520 George E.—M-525 Anna
318.	M-525 Anna—M-532 Petro
319.	M-532 Petro—M-552 William H.
320.	M-552 William H.—M-600 Charles A.
321.	M-600 Charles A.—M-600 Hiram
322.	M-600 Hiram L.—M-600 Mary C.
323.	M-600 Mary C.—M-610 Angelena
324.	M-610 Angelina—M-620 Andy P.
325.	M-620 Angela—M-620 Harry
326.	M-620 Harry—M-620 Maurice L.
327.	M-620 Maurice W.—M-622 Joe
328.	M-622 Joe—M-624 Victoria, Mrs.
329.	M-624 Vincent—M-625 Ralph
330.	M-625 Ralph—M-632 Gertrude
331.	M-632 Gertrude—M-635 Hattie
332.	M-635 Hattie—M-640 Andrew
333.	M-640 Andrew—M-652 Mary
334.	M-652 Mary—M-666 Ruth
335.	N-000 A.—N-150 Joseph B.
336.	N-150 Joseph C.—N-213 Charles
337.	N-213 Charles B.—N-242 Alice
338.	N-242 Alice—N-260 Peter
339.	N-260 Peter—N-400 Daniel
340.	N-400 Daniel—N-425 Mary
341.	N-425 Mary—N-541 Frank
342.	N-542 Albert—N-623 Louis
343.	N-623 Louis—N-665 John
344.	O-000 Adam—O-165 Michael J.
345.	O-165 Michael J.—O-244 John J.
346.	O-244 Katie—O-340 William H.
347.	O-340 William H.—O-431 Jemina
348.	O-431 Jessie—O-540 John
349.	O-540 John—O-632 Stanley
350.	O-632 Stephen—O-665 William J.
351.	P-000 Abesena F.—P-160 Ainger J.
352.	P-160 Albert—P-200 Louie
353.	P-200 Louie—P-235 Charles F.
354.	P-235 Charles M.—P-260 John
355.	P-260 John—P-321 William
356.	P-321 William—P-360 Ad
357.	P-360 Ada—P-362 George
358.	P-362 George—P-362 William
359.	P-362 William—P-400 Mary J.
360.	P-400 Mary J.—P-412 Mike
361.	P-412 Mike—P-420 Vassel
362.	P-420 Vendel—P-450 Frank
363.	P-450 Frank—P-460 Hervey
364.	P-460 Horace—P-525 Vernon
365.	P-525 Virginia—P-600 Edward H.
366.	P-600 Edward H.—P-620 Daniel
367.	P-620 Daniel—P-620 Robert T.
368.	P-620 Robinson C.—P-625 Amer
369.	p-625 Ammelia—P-626 William L.
370.	P-626 William M.—P-636 Margaret
371.	P-636 Margaret—P-660 Jorrn
372.	P-660 Joseph—P-666 Giovanni
373.	Q-000 Abraham F.—Q-660 Pasquale
374.	R-000—R-100 John
375.	R-100 John—R-125 William L.
376.	R-125 William L.—R-152 Hiram
377.	R-152 Hirani—R-162 John
378.	R-162 John—R-163 William P.
379.	R-163 William P.—R-200 Ernest R.
380.	R-200 Ernestina—R-200 John G.
381.	R-200 John G.—R-200 Samuel
382.	R-200 Samuel—R-220 Michael
383.	R-220 Michael—R-240 Franklin A.
384.	R-240 Franklin H.—R-250 Joe
385.	R-250 Joe—R-255 James K.
386.	R-255 Jeanette—R-262 Sarah M.
387.	R-262 Sarrah B.—R-263 William
388.	R-263 William—R-300 James
389.	R-300 James—R-300 William W.
390.	R-300 William W.—R-320 Milton
391.	R-320 Milton—R-340 B. F.

392.	R-340 Banche—R-355 William
393.	R-355 William—R-365 Edward B.
394.	R-365 Edward D.—R-422 George D.
395.	R-422 George H.—R-500 James
396.	R-500 James—R-520 Anthony
397.	R-520 Anthony—R-525 Anna
398.	R-525 Anna E.—R-542 Louis
399.	R-542 Lula—R-556 John
400.	R-556 John— R-620 Jeremiah
401.	R-620 Jesse C.—R-663 Philio
402.	S-000 A.—S-100 Franklin
403.	S-100 Franklin—S-120 David
404.	S-120 David—S-126 John S.
405.	S-126 John W.—S-140 James K.
406.	S-140 James L.—S-150 John B.
407.	S-150 John C.—S-155 Anna M.
408.	S-155 Annie L.—S-160 Harvey G.
409.	S-160 Harvey G.—S-160 Theodore
410.	S-160 Theodore—S-163 Leopold D.
411.	S-163 Leroy—S-200 Eugene G.
412.	S-200 Eugene M.—S-216 Elva M.
413.	S-216 Emanne—S-236 Mahoney Seasli
414.	S-236 Malodia Mary—S-250 Stephen
415.	S-250 Stephen—S-263 Anthony
416.	S-263 Anthony L.—S-300 Leroy W.
417.	S-300 Lester A.—S-312 Michlean
418.	S-312 Mick—S-315 Lucindy
419.	S-315 Lucy—S-316 W. E.
420.	S-316 W. J.—S-320 Ruth
421.	S-320 Ruth E.—S-325 Mary E.
422.	S-325 Mary L.—S-332 Uri V.
423.	S-332 Urias—S-340 Martha J.
424.	S-340 Martha U.—S-346 James
425.	S-346 James—S-350 William
426.	S-350 William—S-352 Nick
427.	S-352 Nick—S-356 Nettie
428.	S-356 Newberry—S-361 Lewis
429.	S-361 Lewis E.—S-362 Mike
430.	S-362 Mike—S-363 John W.
431.	S-363 John W.—S-365 Emma J.
432.	S-365 Emma J.—S-400 Edgar J.
433.	S-400 Edgar J.—S-410 Charles C.
434.	S-410 Charles J.—S-415 Thomas
435.	S-415 Thomas—S-421 Max
436.	S-421 Mayfield—S-432 Anna
437.	S-432 Anna—S-436 Anthony H.
438.	S-436 Anthony J.—S-452 John
439.	S-452 John—S-460 Paul S.
440.	S-460 Paul S.—S-500 Martin
441.	S-500 Martin—S-514 John S.
442.	S-514 John S.—S-520 James
443.	S-520 James—S-524 Adam
444.	S-524 Adam—S-526 John H.
445.	S-526 John H.—S-530 Charles
446.	S-530 Charles—S-530 Frank
447.	S-530 Frank—S-530 Jacob B.
448.	S-530 Jacob B.—S-530 Lloyd
449.	S-530 Lloyd—S-530 Rolla M.
450.	S-530 Rollin C.—S-532 Ada C.
451.	S-532 Ada E.—S-536 Annie B.
452.	S-536 Annie C.—S-536 Jacob
453.	S-536 Jacob—S-536 Thomas
454.	S-536 Thomas—S-543 John
455.	S-543 John—S-552 Elizah
456.	S-552 Ella—S-560 Sylvestian
457.	S-560 Syvida—S-600 Louis E.
458.	S-600 Louis R.—S-616 Belle
459.	S-616 Belle—S-620 Steve
460.	S-620 Steve—S-632 Frank
461.	S-632 Frank—S-640 Thomas C.
462.	S-640 Thomas I.—S-660 Addison
463.	S-660 Addison—S-666 Zigmond
464.	T-000 Abraham—T-200 Joe
465.	T-200 Joe—T-260 Ernest
466.	T-260 Estalla C.—T-350 Andrew
467.	T-350 Andrew—T-455 Mary A.
468.	T-455 Mary A.—T-460 Webster H.
469.	T-460 Webster S.—T-512 Joanna
470.	T-512 Joanna—T-520 Charles L.
471.	T-520 Charles M.—T-520 Mary J.
472.	T-520 Mary J.—T-526 Beatrice
473.	T-526 Benjamin F.—T-600 William P.
474.	T-600 William R.—T-620 Mary H.
475.	T-620 Mary J.—T-630 Lundy W.
476.	T-630 Mabel—T-651 Mary H.

477.	T-651 Mary S.—T-662 Joseph
478.	T-662 Joseph—T-666 Sue L.
479.	U-000 Clyde M.—U-522 Bertha T.
480.	U-522 Charley—U-665 Paul
481.	V-000 Albert—V-250 Benson
482.	V-250 Bert—V-420 John
483.	V-420 John A.—V-520 Joseph W.
484.	V-520 Joseph W.—V-536 Jacob M.
485.	V-536 Jacob P.—V-645 George
486.	V-645 Giovanni—V-665 Willim
487.	W-000 Abram B.—W-160 Frank K.
488.	W-160 Frank L.—W-200 Elmer E.
489.	W-200 Elmer E.—W-220 Stanley
490.	W-220 Stanley—W-240 Frank
491.	W-240 Frank—W-252 Wasnik
492.	W-252 Wassa—W-256 Nettie M.
493.	W-256 Nevada I.—W-300 Elsie A.
494.	W-300 Elsie M.—W-300 Samuel
495.	W-300 Samuel—W-322 Stanley
496.	W-322 Stanley—W-326 Chas.
497.	W-326 Chas.—W-355 Jacob
498.	W-355 Jacob—W-362 Samuel
499.	W-362 Samuel B.—W-410 Clem
500.	W-410 Clemon—W-416 Jesse P.
501.	W-416 Jessie—W-420 John
502.	W-420 John—W-421 Labert C.
503.	W-421 Lawrence—W-425 Harry W.
504.	W-425 Harry W.—W-425 William J.
505.	W-425 William J.—W-430 Henry A.
506.	W-430 Henry B.—W-436 Harry
507.	W-436 Harry—W-452 Agustus
508.	W-452 Agustus—W-452 Jane
509.	W-452 Jane—W-452 William B.
510.	W-452 William C.—W-500 Thomas
511.	W-500 Thomas—W-530 Antonio
512.	W-530 Archie—W-550 Fred
513.	W-550 Fred C.—W-615 Felix
514.	W-615 Fergus—W-624 Abram M.
515.	W-624 Albert—W-635 Emenlia S.
516.	W-635 Emery—W-656 Henry
517.	W-656 Henry—W-666 Linne
518.	X-136 Frank M.—X-660 Henry
519.	Y-000 Abert E.—Y-242 Joseph
520.	Y-242 Joseph—Y-362 John
521.	Y-362 John—Y-520 Joseph
522.	Y-520 Joseph—Y-535 Joseph
523.	Y-535 Lloyd A.—Y-665 Mike
524.	Z-000 Albert—Z-246 Clara E.
525.	Z-246 Clarence—Z-420 Viola
526.	Z-420 Wadick—Z-550 Ivan
527.	Z-550 Joe—Z-630 Daniel
528.	Z-630 Domenick—Z-666 Huery

PHILADELPHIA COUNTY

529.	A-000 Anna—A-342 Elizabeth
530.	A-342 Fannie—A-450 Larry
531.	A-450 Laura—A-620 Christian F.
532.	A-620 D. Harper—A-664 Thos. C.
533.	B-000 Adella—B-230 James
534.	B-230 James—B-260 Elizabeth
535.	B-260 Elizabeth—B-340 Mary
536.	B-340 Mary—B-400 Thomas
537.	B-400 Thomas—B-450 Bryce
538.	B-450 Bryce M.—B-520 Mae
539.	B-520 Magaret—B-560 Mary
540.	B-560 Mary—B-620 Frank
541.	B-620 Frank—B-625 Alveh R.
542.	B-625 Amelia—B-632 George W.
543.	B-632 George W.—B-650 Catherine
544.	B-650 Catherine—B-650 William J.
545.	B-650 William J.—B-655 Ester
546.	B-655 Esther—B-666 John
547.	C-000 A. C., Mrs.—C-200 Harry
548.	C-200 Harry—C-260 Herbert C.
549.	C-260 Hyman—C-416 Jennie E.
550.	C-416 Jesse L.—C-452 John
551.	C-452 John—C-500 Alfred
552.	C-500 Alfred—C-516 Edna
553.	C-516 Edward—C-552 Patrick
554.	C-552 Patrick—C-615 Robert
555.	C-615 Robert—C-625 William T.
556.	C-625 William T.—C-650 Annie
557.	C-650 Annie—C-665 Winford
558.	D-000 Addie—D-140 Alfonso
559.	D-140 Alice—D-235 Ada N.
560.	D-235 Albert A.—D-263 Mary
561.	D-263 Mary—D-410 James

562.	D-410 James E.—D-500 Patrick
563.	D-500 Patrick—D-540 Joseph
564.	D-540 Joseph—D-620 Marry
565.	D-620 Martha—D-665 William
566.	E-000 A. E.—E-263 Fannie E.
567.	E-263 Francis—E-520 William
568.	E-520 William—E-665 Adolph
569.	F-000 Ada—F-260 Jacob
570.	F-260 Jacob—F-425 Samuel H.
571.	F-425 Sara—F-463 John
572.	F-463 John—F-620 Cynes
573.	F-620 Daniel—F-636 George W.
574.	F-636 Gerther—F-655 William
575.	F-655 William—F-666 Sarah
576.	G-000 Ada— G-256 Charles W.
577.	G-256 Clark O.—G-416 James N.
578.	G-416 James R.—G-431 Israel
579.	G-431 Israel—G-521 Berry
580.	G-521 Bessie—G-615 Annie
581.	G-615 Annie—G-630 Josephine
582.	G-630 Josephine—G-650 Sadie
583.	G-650 Sadie—G-666 Matthew
584.	H-000 Adaline—H-163 Enerls
585.	H-163 Eva—H-220 Mary M.
586.	H-220 Mary M.—H-255 James T.
587.	H-255 James T.—H-362 Willard
588.	H-362 William B.—H-426 Michael
589.	H-426 Mike—H-500 Katie
590.	H-500 Khelen—H-530 Della
591.	H-530 Dessa W.—H-556 Joseph
592.	H-556 Leo—H-620 Sarah
593.	H-620 Sarah—H-635 Emil E. T.
594.	H-635 Emil G.—H-663 Timothy
595.	I-000 Buchi—I-663 Nathan
596.	J-000 Allen—J-460 Rosanna
597.	J-460 Sarah—J-523 Wm. B.
598.	J-523 Wm. C.—J-614 Josephine
599.	J-615 August—J-665 John K.
600.	K-000 Abraham—K-246 Philomene
601.	K-246 Raymond—K-400 John J.
602.	K-400 John J.—K-450 Rose
603.	K-450 Rose—K-510 Julius
604.	K-510 Kate—K-530 William
605.	K-530 William—K-621 James
606.	K-621 James—K-666 Geo. T.
607.	L-000 Abraham L.—L-150 Richel D.
608.	L-150 Rock—L-200 Sarah
609.	L-200 Sarah—L-300 Bella
610.	L-300 Belle—L-500 Ellen N.
611.	L-500 Ellen T.—L-522 Horace S.
612.	L-522 Howard—L-600 Herman
613.	L-600 Hesian—L-664 Joseph
614.	M-000—M-210 Lizzie
615.	M-210 Louis—M-225 Catharin
616.	M-225 Catharine—M-240 Charles
617.	M-240 Charles—M-242 Sarah
618.	M-242 Sarah—M-250 Herbert
619.	M-250 Herbert T.—M-253 Mary
620.	M-253 Mary—M-260 Bernard
621.	M-260 Bernard—M-264 Chas.
622.	M-264 Chas. W.—M-325 Mary
623.	M-325 Mary—M-425 Thomas F.
624.	M-425 Thomas L.—M-460 Emma
625.	M-460 Emma—M-500 Maria
626.	M-500 Maria—M-550 Ellen
627.	M-550 Ellen—M-600 Mary J.
628.	M-600 Mary J.—M-620 Evan A.
629.	M-620 Ezekieh—M-625 Charles
630.	M-625 Charles—M-640 Angelo
631.	M-640 Anie—M-665 Marie
632.	N-000 Ada E.—N-300 Thomas
633.	N-300 Walter—N-600 Edward
634.	N-600 Edward—N-665 H.
635.	O-000 Andelo—O-340 James
636.	O-340 James—O-616 Joseph B.
637.	O-616 Vance—O-664 Gertrude
638.	P-000 Abraham L.—P-300 Raphael
639.	P-300 Richard M.—P-400 Hoffman
640.	P-400 Horace—P-456 John J.
641.	P-456 John J.—P-620 Gottlieb
642.	P-620 Grace, Mrs.—P-634 James
643.	P-634 James G.—P-663 William
644.	Q-000 Charles W.—Q-660 James
645.	R-000 A. Pratt—R-152 Peter
646.	R-152 Peter A.—R-200 Louis J.
647.	R-200 Louisa—R-250 Nickolas
648.	R-250 Nowell—R-300 Charles B.

649.	R-300 Charles C.—R-351 B.
650.	R-351 Benj.—R-500 Charles
651.	R-500 Charles—R-543 Walter
652.	R-543 Walter—R-663 Charles
653.	S-000 Abigale—S-143 Peter
654.	S-143 Peter—S-163 Matilda K.
655.	S-163 Mattie A.—S-245 Gisella
656.	S-245 Hans C.—S-315 Jacob
657.	S-315 James—S-336 William
658.	S-336 William—S-353 John
659.	S-353 John—S-363 Mary
660.	S-363 Mary—S-415 Mary
661.	S-415 Mary—S-436 Samuel
662.	S-436 Samuel A. J.—S-512 Edward J.
663.	S-512 Edward L.—S-530 Bapiste
664.	S-530 Bararti—S-530 Lizzie
665.	S-530 Lizzie—S-536 Edward A.
666.	S-536 Edward A.—S-555 Jacob
667.	S-555 Jennie E.—S-625 Solomon
668.	S-625 Stanie—S-665 Paul
669.	T-000 Adrian—T-400 James
670.	T-400 James A.—T-512 J. Viola
671.	T-512 J. Wilmer—T-552 Laura K.
672.	T-552 Lewis L.—T-653 Benjamin
673.	T-653 Benjamin F.—T-666 Luisa I.
674.	U-000 Catharine—U-660 Louisa
675.	V-000 Alberta—V-536 Mary
676.	V-536 Mary—V-662 Samuel
677.	W-000 Alberta—W-240 John
678.	W-240 John—W-300 Lizzie
679.	W-300 Lizzie—W-352 Rex
680.	W-352 Robert—W-420 Frank
681.	W-420 Frank—W-425 Lillian M.
682.	W-425 Lillian S.—W-450 Emma C.
683.	W-450 Emma S.—W-516 Benjiman
684.	W-516 Beorge—W-623 H. Garfield
685.	W-623 Hanna—W-665 Michael
686.	X-160 Frances—X-536 Ida E.
687.	Y-000 A.—Y-665 Antonia
688.	Z-000 Beate—Z-662 Michael

SOUTH CAROLINA   T1275 (Soundex)

1.	A-000—A-352 J.
2.	A-352 K.—A-500 M.
3.	A-500 N.—B-120
4.	B-200—B-251 R.
5.	B-251 S.—B-346 M.
6.	B-346 N.—B-424 I.
7.	B-424 J.—B-500 F.
8.	B-500 G.—B-600 Je
9.	B-600 Ji.—B-622 R.
10.	B-622 S.—B-634 V.
11.	B-634 W.—B-650 He
12.	B-650 Hi.—B-650
13.	B-651—C-100 S.
14.	C-100 T.—C-200 M.
15.	C-200 N.—C-400 O.
16.	C-400 P.—C-455 C.
17.	C-455 D.—C-514 P.
18.	C-514 R.—C-600 I.
19.	C-600 J.—C-634
20.	C-636—D-120 Al
21.	D-120 Am—D-122
22.	D-130—D-251 S.
23.	D-251 T.—D-530 G.
24.	D-530 H.—D-660
25.	E-000—E-400
26.	E-420—F-240
27.	F-250—F-460 C.
28.	F-460 D.—F-626 P.
29.	F-626 R.—G-125 I.
30.	G-125 J.—G-350 M.
31.	G-350 N.—G-450 L.
32.	G-450 M.—G-600 L.
33.	C-600 M.—G-635 C.
34.	G-635 D.—G-650 Q.
35.	G-650 R.—H-125
36.	H-126—H-252 D.
37.	H-252 E.—H-400 A.
38.	H-400 B.—H-452 C.
39.	H-452 D.—H-525 J.
40.	H-525 K.—H-560 J.
41.	H-560 K.—H-630 F.
42.	H-630 G.—I-200 S.
43.	I-200 T.—J-250 Q.

44.	J-250 R.—J-520 Ji
45.	J-520 Jo—J-525 Ch
46.	J-525 Ci—J-525 Ni
47.	J-525 No—K-200 J.
48.	K-200 K.—K-523 Ja
49.	K-523 Je—L-000 V.
50.	L-000 W.—L-240 G.
51.	L-240 H.—L-500
52.	L-510—L-630
53.	L-652—M-200 We
54.	M-200 Wi—M-240 El
55.	M-240 Em—M-250 D.
56.	M-250 E.—M-260 E.
57.	M-260 F.—M-324 P.
58.	M-324 R.—M-452
59.	M-460—M-535
60.	M-540—M-620 C.
61.	M-620 D.—M-635 L.
62.	M-635 M.—N-425 D.
63.	N-425 E.—O-520 A.
64.	O-520 B.—P-320 G.
65.	P-320 H.—P-412
66.	P-420—P-620 D.
67.	P-620 E.—P-632 D.
68.	P-636 E.—R-150
69.	R-152—R-163 J.
70.	R-163 K.—R-251
71.	R-255—R-300
72.	R-320—R-521
73.	R-521—S-163 C.
74.	S-163 D.—S-315 G.
75.	S-315 H.—S-360 K.
76.	S-360 L.—S-420 C.
77.	S-420 D.—S-520 S.
78.	S-520 T.—S-530 James
79.	S-530 James A.—S-536 G.
80.	S-536 H.—S-552 Mas
81.	S-552 Mat—T-260 L.
82.	T-260 S.—T-512 C.
83.	T-512 D.—T-521 L.
84.	T-521 M.—V-000 D.
85.	V-000 E.—W-240 G.
86.	W-240 H.—W-300 L.
87.	W-300 M.—W-350
88.	W-355—W-420 R.
89.	W-420 S.—W-426 K.
90.	W-426 L.—W-452 G.
91.	W-452 H.—W-452 Wa
92.	W-452 We—W-630 G.
93.	W-630 F.—Institutions

TENNESSEE   T1276 (Soundex)
See rolls 112–146 for Chattanooga, Knoxville, Memphis, and Nashville.

1.	A-000—A-352 D.
2.	A-352 E.—A-450 R.
3.	A-450 S.—A-652 E.
4.	A-652 F.—B-212
5.	B-230—B-260 V.
6.	B-260 W.—B-400 B.
7.	B-400 C.—B-421
8.	B-424—B-500 C.
9.	B-500 D.—B-550 V.
10.	B-550 W.—B-620 Q.
11.	B-620 R.—B-630 L.
12.	B-630 M.—B-640
13.	B-642—B-650 Sherman B.
14.	B-650 Sid.—B-653 S.
15.	B-653 T.—C-155 J.
16.	C-155 K.—C-234 M.
17.	C-234 N.—C-400 I.
18.	C-400 J.—G-450 J.
19.	C-450 K.—C-462 R.
20.	C-462 S.—C-536 C.
21.	C-536 D.—C-613 R.
22.	C-613 S.—C-625 Joe T.
23.	C-625 John—C-640 Jinnie
24.	C-640 Joe—D-120 G.
25.	D-120 H.—D-200 F.
26.	D-200 G.—D-300 I.
27.	D-300 J.—D-500
28.	D-510—D-616 L.
29.	D-616 M.—E-240 L.
30.	E-240 M.—E-430
31.	E-436—F-236 L.
32.	F-236 M.—F-436

33.	F-450—F-623 G.
34.	F-623 H.—F-655 S.
35.	F-655 T.—G-321
36.	G-340—G-450 Jim W.
37.	G-450 Joe—G-600
38.	G-610—G-630 Wilie G.
39.	G-630 Will—G-653 G.
40.	G-653 H.—H-200 B.
41.	H-200 C.—H-235 L.
42.	H-235 M.—H-300 Willie N.
43.	H-300 Wilson D.—H-400 B.
44.	H-400 C.—H-400 Wiley M.
45.	H-400 Will—H-463
46.	H-500—H-530 C.
47.	H-530 D.—H-560 B.
48.	H-560 C.—H-621
49.	H-623—H-635 V.
50.	H-635 W.—J-000 K.
51.	J-000 L.—J-520 C.
52.	J-520 D.—J-520 V.
53.	J-520 W.—J-525 Luke
54.	J-525 Lula—K-000 G.
55.	K-000 H.—K-510 K.
56.	K-510 L.—K-600
57.	K-610—L-140 Jim T.
58.	L-140 Joe—L-240
59.	L-250—L-400 V.
60.	L-400 W.—L-522 Jim P.
61.	L-522 Jody—M-140
62.	M-150—M-216 Q.
63.	M-216 R.—M-243 I.
64.	M-243 J.—M-252 I.
65.	M-252 J.—M-265 F.
66.	M-265 G.—M-350
67.	M-360—M-460 Jimmie
68.	M-460 Joab G.—M-550 L.
69.	M-550 M.—M-610 G.
70.	M-610 H.—M-625 R.
71.	M-625 S.—N-100 I.
72.	N-100 J.—N-410
73.	N-425—O-210 M.
74.	O-210 N.—O-600
75.	P-000—P-320 C.
76.	P-320 D.—P-400
77.	P-410—P-520 M.
78.	P-520 N.—P-620 Q.
79.	P-620 R.—P-630 Job
80.	P-630 Joe—R-000 S.
81.	R-000 T.—R-163 Johathan
82.	R-163 John—R-230 P.
83.	R-230 R.—R-263 J.
84.	R-263 K.—R-350
85.	R-360—R-530 K.
86.	R-530 L.—S-152 L.
87.	S-152 M.—S-300 F.
88.	S-300 G.—S-330 F.
89.	S-330 G.—S-361 J..
90.	S-361 K.—S-410 V.
91.	S-410 W.—S-512 J.
92.	S-512 M.—S-530 Gertrude
93.	S-530 Gideon T.—S-530 Thirl
94.	S-530 Thom E.—S-552 I.
95.	S-552 J.—S-650 E.
96.	S-650 F.—T-350
97.	T-400—T-460 Whig
98.	T-460 Wiley—T-520 V.
99.	T-520 W.—T-650 I.
100.	T-650 J.—V-250
101.	V-251—W-160 P.
102.	W-160 R.—W-300 F.
103.	W-300 G.—W-320 S.
104.	W-320 T.—W-356
105.	W-360—W-420 M.
106.	W-420 N.—W-425
107.	W-426—W-452 A.
108.	W-452 B.—W-452 R.
109.	W-452 S.—W-610
110.	W-620—W-650 R.
111.	W-650 S.—Inst.

TENNESSEE CITIES: Chattanooga, Knoxville, Memphis, and Nashville

112.	A-000—B-166
113.	B-200—B-424
114.	B-425—B-626
115.	B-630—B-666
116.	C-000—C-455

117. C-456—C-635
118. C-636—D-324
119. D-325—E-366
120. E-400—F-625
121. F-626—G-516
122. G-520—H-160
123. H-200—H-400
124. H-410—H-620
125. H-621—J-520 Jordan
126. J-520 Joseph—K-400
127. K-410—L-232
128. L-235—M-212
129. M-213—M-300
130. M-320—M-600
131. M-610—N-614
132. N-620—P-413
133. P-420—R-150
134. R-152—R-360
135. R-361—S-315
136. S-316—S-520
137. S-521—S-653
138. S-655—T-626
139. T-630—W-300 M.
140. W-300 N.—W-426 K.
141. W-426 L.—W-500
142. W-510— End of State

TEXAS   T1277 (Soundex)

1. A-000—A-235 I.
2. A-235 J.—A-325 M.
3. A-325 N.—A-362
4. A-363—A-425 L.
5. A-425 M.—A-450 L.
6. A-450 M.—A-535 K.
7. A-535 L.—A-536 Q.
8. A-536 R.—A-651
9. A-652—B-150 Mary
10. B-150 Matthew—B-200 Smith
11. B-200 Sofa—B-240 F.
12. B-240 G.—B-256 Levy
13. B-256 Lewis—B-300 Emily
14. B-300 Emma—B-341
15. B-342—B-400 E.
16. B-400 F.—B-415
17. B-416—B-424 Oscar
18. B-424 Owen—B-450 I.
19. B-450 J.—B-463 L.
20. B-463 M.—B-520 O.
21. B-520 P.—B-533
22. B-534—B-600 H.
23. B-600 I.—B-620 Edwin W.
24. B-620 Effie—B-620 T.
25. B-620 U.—B-625 K.
26. B-625 L.—B-630 O.
27. B-630 P.—B-634 M.
28. B-634 N.—B-640
29. B-641—B-650 Govesner
30. B-650 Grace—B-650 O.
31. B-650 P.—B-652 H.
32. B-652 I.—B-653 K.
33. B-653 L.—B-660 Jimmy W.
34. B-660 Joaquin—C-145 G.
35. C-145 H.—C-165
36. C-166-C-200 Phil
37. C-200 Philip—C-240 Q.
38. C-240 R.—C-325
39. C-326—C-400 R.
40. C-400 S.—C-430 D.
41. C-430 E.—C-452 A.
42. C-452 J.—C-455 S.
43. C-455 T.—C-462 V.
44. C-462 W.—C-514 D.
45. C-514 E.—C-530 E.
46. C-530 F.—C-552 A.
47. C-552 B.—C-600 Jodie
48. C-600 Joe—C-616 I.
49. C-616 J.—C-623 A.
50. C-623 B.—C-632 L.
51. C-632 M.—C-636 Robt. L.
52. C-636 Robt. M.—C-650 James
53. C-650 James A.—D-000 Jonie
54. D-000 Joseph—D-120 H.
55. D-120 I.—D-120 T.
56. D-120 U.—D-160 V.
57. D-160 W.—D-242 C.
58. D-242 D.—D-260 L.

59. D-260 M.—D-400 B.
60. D-400 C.—D-460 R.
61. D-460 S.—D-520 John
62. D-520 Johnie—D-540 V.
63. D-540 W.—D-610 R.
64. D-610 S.—D-650 V.
65. D-650 W.—E-156
66. E-160—E-242 R.
67. E-242 S.—E-363 I.
68. E-363 J.—E-426
69. E-430—E-536
70. E-540—F-226
71. F-230—F-300
72. F-310—F-430 R.
73. F-430 S.—F-460 B.
74. F-460 C.—F-520 D.
75. F-520 E.—F-620 F.
76. F-620 G.—F-630 E.
77. F-630 F.—F-652 E.
78. F-652 F.—F-656 G.
79. F-656 H.—G-152 V.
80. G-152 W.—G-300 I.
81. G-300 J.—G-360 M.
82. G-360 N.—G-420 I.
83. G-420 J.—G-450 Josephine
84. G-450 Juan—G-520 L.
85. G-520 M.—G-530 K.
86. G-530 L.—G-600 Roqus
87. G-600 Rosa—G-615 R.
88. G-615 S.—G-620 Jake L.
89. G-620 James—G-620 Void
90. G-620 W.—G-630 Ruth
91. G-630 S.—G-650 D.
92. G-650 E.—G-650
93. G-651—G-660 I.
94. G-660 J.—H-153
95. H-153—H-200 F.
96. H-200 G.—H-220 E.
97. H-220 F.—H-245
98. H-246—H-260 N.
99. H-260 O.—H-322 I.
100. H-322 J.—H-360
101. H-361—H-400 J. Y.
102. H-400 Jack—H-400 S.
103. H-400 T.—H-430 Jones
104. H-430 Joseph—H-453 R.
105. H-453 S.—H-516 H.
106. H-516 I.—H-524 B.
107. H-524 C.—H-536 Anna
108. H-536 Annie—H-542
109. H-543—H-560 Will
110. H-560 William—H-620 D.
111. H-620 E.—H-620 Zu
112. H-621—H-630 George
113. H-630 Georgia—H-635 C.
114. H-635 D.—H-650 V.
115. H-650 W.—H-660 I.
116. H-660 J.—J-146
117. J-150—J-250 Elizabeth
118. J-250 Ella—J-250 William
119. J-250 William—J-520 Dawson
120. J-520 J.—J-520 Jorden
121. J-520 Jose—J-520 Tollie F.
122. J-520 Tom—J-525 Charlet
123. J-525 Charley—J-525 James
124. J-525 James A.—J-525 Patty
125. J-525 Paul—J-552 R.
126. J-552 S.—J-126
127. K-130—K-325 G.
128. K-325 H.—K-420 I.
129. K-420 J.—K-510 M.
130. K-510 N.—K-520 Sandy
131. K-520 Sara—K-536 V.
132. K-536 W.—K-625
133. K-625—L-000 Levi
134. L-000 Levy—L-120 O.
135. L-120 P.—L-200 Bee
136. L-200 Bell—L-200 Moe
137. L-200 Mollie—L-236 H.
138. L-236 I.—L-300 A.
139. L-300 B.—L-360 G.
140. L-360 J.—L-500 N.
141. L-500 O.—L-520 M.
142. L-520 N.—L-532 K.
143. L-532 L.—L-600 I.
144. L-600 J.—M-000
145. M-100—M-200 I.

146. M-200 J.—M-210
147. M-211—M-232 I.
148. M-232 J.—M-240 D.
149. M-240 E.—M-243 R.
150. M-243 S.—M-250 A.
151. M-250 B.—M-250
152. M-251—M-254 L.
153. M-254 M.—M-262 G.
154. M-262 H.—M-300
155. M-310—M-324 I.
156. M-324 J.—M-360 I.
157. M-360 J.—M-434
158. M-435—M-460 B.
159. M-460 C.—M-460 V.
160. M-460 W.—M-520
161. M-521—M-535 K.
162. M-535 L.—M-600 D.
163. M-600 E.—M-600 M.
164. M-600 N.—M-620 Anne Mary
165. M-620 Annie—M-620 V.
166. M-620 W.—M-625 G.
167. M-625 N.—M-635 E.
168. M-635 F.—M-635 Sc
169. M-635 Se—M-666
170. N-000—N-242 B.
171. N-242 C.—N-366
172. N-400—N-450 L.
173. N-450 M.—N-635 D.
174. N-635 E.—O-254
175. O-255—O-435
176. O-436—O-632 Margurite
177. O-632 Maria—P-200 Jake
178. P-200 James—P-300 Eljas
179. P-300 Ella—P-355 L.
180. P-355 M.—P-400 Angeline
181. P-400 Ann—P-412 Lily
182. P-412 Lina—P-454
183. P-455—P-520 K.
184. P-520 L.—P-600 Rodney
185. P-600 Rosa—P-620 Jourdan
186. P-620 Joy—P-624 Jim S.
187. P-624 Joe—P-626 Matt
188. P-626 Matthew—P-636 M.
189. P-636 N.—R-000 E.
190. R-000 F.—R-140 I.
191. R-140 J.—R-160 L.
192. R-160 M.—R-163 L.
193. R-163 M.—R-200 F.
194. R-200 G.—R-200 S.
195. R-200 T.—R-240 K.
196. R-240 L.—R-261
197. R-262—R-263 S.
198. R-263 T.—R-320 F.
199. R-320 G.—R-352
200. R-353—R-400 D.
201. R-400 E.—R-500 Oscar
202. R-500 T.—R-534 D.
203. R-534 E.—R-562 I.
204. R-562 J.—S-120 R.
205. S-120 S.—S-152
206. S-153—S-163 Q.
207. S-163 R.—S-250 L.
208. S-250 M.—S-300 Rector
209. S-300 Red—S-315 M.
210. S-315 Matt.—S-326
211. S-330—S-350 Jake
212. S-350 James—S-360 I.
213. S-360 J.—S-363 J.
214. S-363 K.—S-400 J.
215. S-400 K.—S-420 M.
216. S-420 N.—S-435
217. S-436—S-500 K.
218. S-500 L.—S-520 Johanna
219. S-520 John—S-526 I.
220. S-526 J.—S-530 Elzy
221. S-530 Emaline—S-530 Johanna
222. S-530 John—S-530 Q.
223. S-530 R.—S-532 D.
224. S-532 E.—S-536 R.
225. S-536 S.—S-552 R.
226. S-552 S.—S-616 G.
227. S-616 H.—S-643
228. S-650—T-234
229. T-235—T-350 K.
230. T-350 L.—T-460 Clain
231. T-460 Clara—T-460 Tidia
232. T-460 Tim—T-512 Max

233. T-512 May—T-520 Jodie
234. T-520 Joe—T-536
235. T-540—T-615
236. T-616—T-650 H.
237. T-650 I.—T-656 M.
238. T-656 N.—V-236
239. V-240—V-456 K.
240. V-456 L.—V-620 M.
241. V-620 N.—W-200 D.
242. W-200 E.—W-246
243. W-250—W-266
244. W-300—W-300 John G.
245. W-300 John H.—W-314
246. W-315—W-325 John
247. W-325 John A.—W-350 K.
248. W-350 L.—W-400 I.
249. W-400 J.—W-420 F.
250. W-420 G.—W-422
251. W-423—W-425 L.
252. W-425 M.—W-426 James
253. W-426 James A.—W-436 Franz
254. W-436 Fred—W-452 Dianah
255. W-452 Dick—W-452 John
256. W-452 John A.—W-452 Sao
257. W-452 Sara—W-514 I.
258. W-514 J.—W-620 G.
259. W-620 H.—W-630 John R.
260. W-630 John S.—W-656
261. W-660—Y-520
262. Y-521—Institutions

VIRGINIA T1278 (Miracode)

1. A-000—A-262 Orwan
2. A-262 Other—A-413 Lydie
3. A-413 Mildred—A-450 Tekfek
4. A-450 Temple—A-536 Lillian B.
5. A-536 Lillie—A-652 Robert M.
6. A-652 Robert O.—A-663 William L.
7. B-000—B-210 Henry T.
8. B-210 Henry W.—B-256 Carl
9. B-256 Carter—B-300 John W.
10. B-300 John W.—B-360 Adelvdrt
11. B-360 Albert M.—B-400 Thomas
12. B-400 Thomas—B-426 Floyd
13. B-426 Frances—B-453 Mandy J.
14. B-453 Mannie—B-520 James
15. B-520 James—B-550 Isaac
16. B-550 Isaac—B-620 Brewer V.
17. B-620 Bridget E.—B-620 Thomas S.
18. B-620 Thomas W.—B-626 Frank M.
19. B-626 Fred—B-634 Banche
20. B-634 Banks—B-642 John
21. B-642 John—B-650 Joeph A.
22. B-650 John—B-650 William
23. B-650 William—B-653 Lindy J.
24. B-653 Lindy J.—B-665 William
25. C-000—C-160 C. C.
26. C-160 C. C.—C-200 Polley
27. C-200 Polly—C-320 Estella
28. C-320 Eugene—C-413 William D.
29. C-413 William E.—C-450 Amanda
30. C-450 Amanda J.—C-455 Philip
31. C-455 Philip—C-462 William
32. C-462 William—C-516 William
33. C-516 William—C-560 William
34. C-560 William—C-616 Isaac W.
35. C-616 Isabell—C-623 William H.
36. C-623 William H.—C-636 Emma
37. C-636 Emma—C-640 Nettie
38. C-640 Nettie—C-666 William
39. D-000—D-120 Lee
40. D-120 Lee—D-160 Edward
41. D-160 Edward—D-250 Mary
42. D-250 Mary—D-340 Walter W.
43. D-340 Ward—D-500 Charlie P.
44. D-500 Charlie S.—D-535 Thomas
45. D-535 Thomas—D-635 Edward J.
46. D-635 Edward R.—D-666 Maria
47. E-000—E-240 Abram
48. E-240 Abram—E-363 Rut
49. E-363 Ruth—E-513 Olin
50. E-514 Bertah—E-663 Wythe C.
51. F-000 Abraham C.—F-300 Daswell
52. F-300 David—F-430 Wm.
53. F-430 Wm. A.—F-462 Amanda
54. F-462 Andrew D.—F-620 Robert

55. F-620 Robert E.—F-640 Oscar
56. F-640 Oscar—F-665 Oscat
57. G-000—G-300 Fracis
58. G-300 Frances—G-400 Victor
59. G-400 Vinetta—G-450 Lionia
60. G-450 Lishe—G-600 Frank
61. G-600 Frank—G-616 Jacob A.
62. G-616 Jacob B.—G-635 Edward
63. G-635 Edward—G-650 Nora
64. G-650 Norama—G-666 Verna
65. H-000—H-163 Olivia E.
66. H-163 Opie—H-220 Ella
67. H-220 Ella—H-252 John
68. H-252 John—H-322 Oscar C.
69. H-322 Oscar G.—H-400 Alice
70. H-400 Alice—H-400 Maggie D.
71. H-400 Magie—H-430 Robert A.
72. H-430 Robert B.—H-500 Charles
73. H-500 Charles—H-524 John
74. H-524 John—H-536 Robert
75. H-536 Robert—H-610 John
76. H-610 John—H-620 Mabel
77. H-620 Mabel—H-626 John
78. H-626 John—H-635 Wm. B.
79. H-635 Wm. L.—H-663 Tomy
80. I-000—I-656 Lizzie
81. J-000—J-250 George
82. J-250 George—J-500 Charlie
83. J-500 Charlie—J-520 Gustans
84. J-520 Gustava—J-520 Nip
85. J-520 Noah—J-525 Alice
86. J-525 Alice—J-525 Jackson T.
87. J-525 Jacob—J-525 Robert
88. J-525 Robert—J-635 Agnes
89. J-635 Agnes—J-660 Percy
90. K-000—K-400 Fred C.
91. K-400 Frederick—K-520 Elsie M.
92. K-520 Emaline—K-610 Edward
93. K-610 Edward—K-666 Annie
94. L-000—L-135 James
95. L-135 James B.—L-200 Kate
96. L-200 Kate—L-236 Olivia
97. L-236 Ollie Mae—L-350 Florce
98. L-350 Florrie—L-516 Willie G.
99. L-516 Willie I.—L-535 Ameda
100. L-535 Andrew—L-665 Waldon
101. M-000—M-200 Mary
102. M-200 Mary—M-235 Pattie
103. M-235 Pearl—M-250 Douglas
104. M-250 Douglas—M-260 Arthur C.
105. M-260 Arthur E.—M-320 John A.
106. M-320 John A.—M-360 Nellie
107. M-360 Nina C.—M-456 Muco
108. M-456 Nat—M-500 Josephine
109. M-500 Josephine—M-560 Annie
110. M-560 Annie—M-600 Richard
111. M-600 Richard—M-620 Joseph
112. M-620 Joseph—M-625 James E.
113. M-625 James E.—M-635 Nannie
114. M-635 Nannie—M-665 Nathaniel J.
115. N-000—N-253 Jesse R.
116. N-253 John—N-540 John
117. N-540 John—N-665 P. R.
118. O-000—O-452 D. T.
119. O-452 David—O-665 Gideon D.
120. P-000—P-250 Sarah
121. P-250 Simeon—P-362 James
122. P-362 James—P-412 Fannie
123. P-412 Fannie M.—P-463 William L. K.
124. P-463 William R.—P-536 Peter
125. P-536 Peter C.—P-620 John M.
126. P-620 John M.—P-625 Robey
127. P-625 Robt.—P-636 Fred
128. P-636 Fred—P-666 Tom
129. Q-000 Virginia—Q-662 Lucy
130. R-000—R-152 Gladis
131. R-152 Gladys—R-163 J. W.
132. R-163 J. W.—R-200 Marion
133. R-200 Marion N.—R-251 George
134. R-251 George—R-300 Amos
135. R-300 Amos—R-320 Thomas
136. R-320 Thomas—R-430 Wilbert
137. R-430 Wilhelmina—R-534 Hannah
138. R-534 Hanry—R-663 William A.
139. S-000—S-146 Caroline
140. S-146 Charles—S-163 Robert

141. S-163 Robert—S-300 Emma J.
142. S-300 Emma Jane—S-315 Henry
143. S-315 Henry—S-340 Edward
144. S-340 Edward—S-354 Samuel H.
145. S-354 Samuel H.—S-363 W. Euhine
146. S-363 W. H.—S-426 Buck
147. S-426 Bullah—S-500 John H.
148. S-500 John J.—S-530 Abrander
149. S-530 Absolom T.—S-530 Henry B.
150. S-530 Henry B.—S-530 Pauline
151. S-530 Pauline—S-536 Emery
152. S-536 Emily—S-560 Isaac M.
153. S-560 Isas H.—S-632 Maud
154. S-632 May W.—S-666 George P.
155. T-000—T-300 James C.
156. T-300 James E.—T-460 David
157. T-460 David A.—T-460 Sam
158. T-460 Sam—T-512 Virginia
159. T-512 Virginia D.—T-520 Stanton
160. T-520 Stella—T-612 Andy
161. T-612 Anliza—T-653 Thomas J.
162. T-653 Thomas R.—T-666 Leah
163. U-000—U-663 Rufus
164. V-000—V-525 T.
165. V-525 Tancy J.—V-660 John P.
166. W-000—W-230 Walter W.
167. W-230 Walter W.—W-300 Arthur
168. W-300 Arthur—W-300 Lizzie
169. W-300 Lizzie—W-320 John
170. W-320 John—W-330 Florence
171. W-330 Florence—W-363 Ship
172. W-363 Ship W.—W-420 Mernitt
173. W-420 Mesey—W-425 Montgomery
174. W-425 More—W-426 Thomas, Sr.
175. W-426 Thomas—W-452 Bettie
176. W-452 Bettie—W-452 Mary M.
177. W-452 Mary, Mrs.—W-500 Withi
178. W-500 Wm. B.—W-620 Vilsa
179. W-620 Virginia—W-635 Henry A.
180. W-635 Henry B.—W-664 Dave
181. X-200 Algie—X-636 Larua
182. Y-000—Y-656 Heln
183. Z-000 Barbara A.—Z-656 Marlin

WEST VIRGINIA T1279 (Miracode)

1. A-000—A-340 Lacy
2. A-340 Louis D.—A-524 Coinnie
3. A-524 Cosbie—A-663 William
4. B-000—B-236 Edward
5. B-236 Edward—B-325 George H. A.
6. B-325 George W.—B-420 Edward
7. B-420 Edward—B-460 Eugene
8. B-460 Fannie—B-550 Jessie
9. B-550 Joe—B-620 Simon
10. B-620 Sjomjeo—B-633 John
11. B-633 John—B-650 Nelson H.
12. B-650 Nancy C.—B-660 Mary B.
13. B-660 Melivin—B-666 Edward
14. C-000—C-200 Hubert W.
15. C-200 Hurman—C-340 Skid C.
16. C-340 Smith—C-436 Francis
17. C-436 Francis Marion—C-500 Effie S.
18. C-500 Eichard—C-540 Lucy
19. C-540 Lucy M.—C-615 John W.
20. C-615 Johnson—C-632 Margait
21. C-632 Mariano—C-665 Philip
22. D-000—D-150 Estella
23. D-150 Estry E.—D-320 John
24. D-320 John—D-500 Virginia
25. D-500 Virginia—D-620 Samuel H.
26. D-620 Samuel W.—D-665 John
27. E-000 Amanda—E-416 Rile
28. E-416 Sarah—E-664 Sady
29. F-000 A. R.—F-423 Geo.
30. F-423 Henry—F-600 Ailen
31. F-600 Ala—F-640 William A.
32. F-640 William C.—F-666 Roy R.
33. G-000 Abbie—G-400 Anna
34. G-400 Antonio—G-530 William G.
35. G-530 William S.—G-626 Harry
36. G-626 Harry—G-666 Mary J.
37. H-000—H-200 Maggie S.
38. H-200 Mahelia—H-255 Edw L.
39. H-255 Edw L.—H-362 Herbert
40. H-362 Herman—H-423 Ethel

41.	H-423 Eugenia—H-520 Silvester
42.	H-520 Sletta—H-553 David W.
43.	H-553 Delorias J.—H-623 James
44.	H-623 James—H-655 Kate
45.	H-655 Kelly—H-662 Sampson M.
46.	I-000—I-663 Salvaton
47.	J-000 Aborn L.—J-520 Francis D.
48.	J-520 Francis L.—J-525 Kate
49.	J-525 Kate—J-663 Owen
50.	K-000—K-400 Mary
51.	K-400 Mary—K-523 Lewis
52.	K-523 Lewis H.—K-663 Lewis
53.	L-000—L-200 John
54.	L-200 John—L-300 Hadden
55.	L-300 Harmon N.—L-520 Dominic
56.	L-520 Donald—L-625 Ed F.
57.	L-625 Edward—L-665 William T.
58.	M-000—M-216 Willie
59.	M-216 Willie T.—M-244 Samuel H.
60.	M-244 Samuel H.—M-254 James
61.	M-254 James—M-320 O. R.
62.	M-320 Odell—M-430 Sarah
63.	M-430 Shade—M-460 Walter
64.	M-460 Walter C.—M-600 Cecel
65.	M-600 Cecie—M-620 James W.
66.	M-620 James W.—M-635 Alpha
67.	M-635 Alugh P.—M-666 Eguat
68.	N-000—N-400 Jesse
69.	N-400 Jessie G.—N-665 Cestea
70.	O-000—O-662 Thomas
71.	P-000—P-350 John W.
72.	P-350 Jora—P-420 Paul
73.	P-420 Paul—P-600 Robert
74.	P-600 Robert—P-626 J. B.
75.	P-626 J. E.—P-665 Jacob
76.	Q-000 George—Q-660 Cora E.
77.	R-000—R-163 John
78.	R-163 John—R-240 Emily
79.	R-240 Emma—R-300 Samuel M.
80.	R-300 Samuel R.—R-452 Willie
81.	R-452 Wilson—R-666 Louie
82.	S-000—S-160 Ray M.
83.	S-160 Ray O.—S-300 Barn
84.	S-300 Barnest—S-332 Roy
85.	S-332 Sam—S-356 Mary
86.	S-356 Mary A.—S-400 Orvil
87.	S-400 Oscar—S-510 J. P.
88.	S-510 Jacob—S-530 Ferry
89.	S-530 Finley—S-530 Wilson W.
90.	S-530 Winbert—S-560 John D.
91.	S-560 John M.—S-653 Malka
92.	S-653 Martha—S-663 Thomas J.
93.	T-000 Benjamin C.—T-460 Clabron
94.	T-460 Clair—T-520 Elsa C.
95.	T-520 Elvin—T-640 Joseph Z.
96.	T-640 Judge G.—T-665 Oswell
97.	U-000 Carl—U-656 Eston
98.	V-000—V-663 John
99.	W-000—W-256 Albert
100.	W-256 Albert—W-320 Thomas
101.	W-320 Thomas E.—W-410 Elias T.
102.	W-410 Elie—W-425 Lawrence
103.	W-426 Lawrence K.—W-452 Harry B.
104.	W-452 Harry E.—W-600 Zilla
105.	W-610 Claud—W-660 William A.
106.	X-234 Jackson—X-652 W. R.
107.	Y-000 Albert—Y-662 James T.
108.	Z-000 Albert—Z-660 Steve

Appendix I

Guide to the Soundex/Miracode System

The Soundex/Miracode filing system, alphabetic for the first letter of surname and numeric thereunder as indicated by divider cards, keeps together names of the same and similar sounds but of variant spellings.

To search for a particular name, you must first work out the code number for the surname of the individual. No number is assigned to the first letter of the surname. If the name is Kuhne, for example, the index card will be in the "K" segment of the index. The code number for Kuhne, worked out according to the system below, is 500.

Soundex Coding Guide

Code	Key Letters and Equivalents
1	b,p,f,v
2	c,s,k,g,j,q,x,z
3	d,t
4	l
5	m,n
6	r

The letters a, e, i, o, u, y, w, and h are *not* coded.
The first letter of a surname is *not* coded.

Every Soundex/Miracode number must be a 3-digit number. A name yielding no code numbers, as Lee, would thus be L000; one yielding only one code number would have two zeros added, as Kuhne, coded as K500; and one yielding two code numbers would have one zero added, as Ebell, coded as E140. Not more than three digits are used, so Ebelson would be coded as E142, *not* E1425.

When two key letters or equivalents appear together, or one key letter immediately follows or precedes an equivalent, the two are coded as one letter, by a single number, as follows: Ke*ll*y, coded as K400; Buer*ck*, coded as B620; *Ll*oyd, coded as L300; and S*ch*aefer, coded as S160.

If several surnames have the same code, the cards for them are arranged alphabetically by given name. There are divider cards showing most code numbers, but not all. For instance, one divider may be numbered 350 and the next one 400. Between the two divider cards there may be names coded 353, 350, 360, 365, and 355, but instead of being in numerical order they are interfiled alphabetically by given name.

Such prefixes to surnames as "van," "Von," "Di," "de," "le," "Di," "D'," "dela," or "du" are sometimes disregarded in alphabetizing and in coding.

The following names are examples of Soundex/Miracode coding and are given only as illustrations.

Name	Letters Coded	Code No.
Allricht	l,r,c	A 462
Eberhard	b,r,r	E 166
Engebrethson	n,g,b	E 521
Heimbach	m,b,c	H 512
Hanselmann	n,s,l	H 524
Henzelmann	n,z,l	H 524
Hildebrand	l,d,b	H 431
Kavanagh	v,n,g	K 152
Lind, Van	n,d	L 530
Lukaschowsky	k,s,s	L 222
McDonnell	c,d,n	M 235
McGee	c	M 200
O'Brien	b,r,n	O 165
Opnian	p,n,n	O 155
Oppenheimer	p,n,m	O 155
Riedemanas	d,m,n	R 355
Zita	t	Z 300
Zitzmeinn	t,z,m	Z 325

Native Americans, Orientals, and Religious Nuns

Researchers using the Soundex/Miracode system to locate religious nuns or persons with American Indian or oriental names should be aware of the way such names were coded. Variations in coding differed from the normal coding system.

Phonetically spelled oriental and Indian names were sometimes coded as if one continuous name, or, if a distinguishable surname was given, the names were coded in the normal manner. For example, the American Indian name Shinka-Wa-Sa may have been coded as "Shinka" (S520) or "Sa" (S000). Researchers should investigate the various possibilities of coding such names.

Religious nun names were coded as if "Sister" was their surname, and they appear in each State's Soundex/Miracode under the code "S236." Within the State's Soundex/Miracode code S236, the names are not necessarily in alphabetical order.

Appendix II

Relationship Terms and Abbreviations (Not in strict alphabetical order)

Adopted	Ad
Adopted Child	Ad.Cl
Adopted Daughter	Ad.D
Adopted Grandchild	Ad.Gcl
Adopted Mother	Ad.M
Adopted Son	Ad.S
Apprentice	Ap
Attendant	At
Assistant	Asst
Aunt	A
Aunt-In-Law	Al
Bartender	Bar
Boarder	Bo
Bound Girl	B.Girl
Bound Boy	B.Boy
Boy	Boy
Brother	B
Brother-In Law	Bl
Butler	Bu
Captain	Cap
Chamber Maid	Cha
Child	Cl
Coachman	Coa
Companion	Com
Cook	Cook
Cousin	C
Cousin-In-Law	Cil
Daughter	D
Daughter-In-Law	Dl
Day Laborer	Dla
Dish Washer	Dw
Domestic	Dom
Employee	Emp
Engineer	En
Farm Hand	Fa.H
Farm Laborer	Fa.L

Farm Worker	Fa.W
Father	F
Father-In-Law	Fl
Fireman	Fi
First Cousin	First C
Foster Brother	Fo.B
Foster Sister	Fo.Si
Foster Son	Fo.S
God Child	God Cl
Governess	Go
Grand Child	Gcl
Grand Daughter	Gd
Grand Father	Gf
Grand Mother	GM
Grand Mother-In-Law	Gml
Grand Son	Gs
Grand Son-In-Law	Gsl
Great Grandfather	Ggf
Grand Niece (same as Great Niece)	Gni
Grand Nephew (same as Great Nephew)	Gn
Great Grandmother	Ggm
Great-Great-Grandfather	Gggf
Great-Great-Grandmother	Gggm
Guardian	Gua
Guest	Guest
Half Sister	H.Si
Half Sister-In-Law	H.Sil
Half Brother	Hb
Half Brother-In-Law	Hbl
Help	Help
Herder	He
Hired Girl	H.Gi
Hired Hand	H.H
Hireling	Hlg
Housekeeper	Hk
Housemaid	H.Maid
House Worker	Hw

Husband	Husband	Ward	Ward
Inmate	Inmate	Warden	Wa
Laborer	La	Wife	W
Laundry	Lau	Workman	Wkm
Lodger	L		
Maid	Maid		

Husband .... Husband
Inmate .... Inmate
Laborer .... La
Laundry .... Lau
Lodger L
Maid .... Maid
Manager .... Man
Matron .... Mat
Mother .... M
Mother-In-Law .... Ml
Nephew .... N
Nephew-In-Law .... Nl
Niece .... Ni
Niece-In-Law .... Nil
Nurse .... Nu
Officer .... O
Partner .... Pa
Patient .... P
Physician .... Ph
Porter .... Por
Principal .... Pri
Prisoner .... Pr
Private .... Prv
Pupil .... Pu
Roomer .... R
Sailor .... Sa
Saleslady .... Sal
Servant .... Se
Servant's Child .... Se.Cl
Sister .... Si
Son .... S
Son-In-Law .... Sl
Step Brother .... Sb
Step Brother-In-Law .... Sbl
Step Child .... Scl
Step Daughter .... Sd
Step Daughter-In-Law .... Sdl
Step Father .... Sf
Step Father-In-Law .... Sfl
Step Granddaughter .... Sgd
Step Grandson .... Sgs
Step Mother .... Sm
Step Mother-In-Law .... Sml
Step Sister .... Ssi
Step Sister-In-Law .... Ssil
Step Son .... Ss
Step Son-In-Law .... Ssl
Superintendent .... Su
Tenant .... Ten
Uncle .... U
Uncle-In-Law .... Ul
Visitor Vi
Waiter .... Wt
Waitress .... Wai

Ward .... Ward
Warden .... Wa
Wife .... W
Workman .... Wkm

Translation of Relationship Terms Given in Spanish (Not in alphabetical order)

Jefe .... Head
Marido .... Husband
Esposa .... Wife
Mujer .... Wife, woman
Nino .... Child
Hijo .... Son
Hija .... Daughter
Padre .... Father
Madre .... Mother
Hermano .... Brother
Hermana .... Sister
Tio .... Uncle
Tia .... Aunt
Sobrino .... Nephew
Sobrina .... Niece
Madrastra .... Step - mother
Hyastra .... Step - Daughter
Hermano de leche .... Foster Brother
Ama de cria .... Foster mother
Hijanuera .... Daughter-in-law
Hijoyerno .... Son-in-law
Yerno .... Son-in-law
Cunada .... Sister-in-law
Cunhada .... Sister-in-law
Cunado .... Brother-in-law
Abuelo .... Grandfather
Abuela .... Grandmother
Bisahuelo .... Great-Grandfather
Bianieto .... Great-grandson
Nieta .... Grandchild
Prino (a) .... Cousin
Ado .... Adopted
Institutriz .... Governess
Criada .... Servant or nurse
Ninera .... Nurse
Cuidar .... Nurse
Criar .... Nurse
Cuarto de los ninos .... Nurse
Alojado .... Lodger
Huesped .... Guest
Pensionista .... Boarder
Pupilo .... Boarder
Huesped .... Boarder
Suegro .... Father-in-law
Interna .... Resident
Blanco .... White
Granjero .... Farmer
Ageno .... Alien

41

Extrano	....	Alien
Extranero	....	Alien
Preso	....	Prisoner
Discipulo	....	Pupil
Paciente	....	Patient
Manicomio	....	Insane Asylum
Municipio	....	County

Bario	....	City
Calle	....	Street

B—Blanco–White

N—Negro–Black

H—Female

V—Male

Appendix III

Enumeration Districts Within Cities Having Populations of 50,000 or More

STATE	CITY	COUNTY	ENUMERATION DISTRICTS
Alabama	Birmingham	Jefferson	42-104, 129-136, 154
	Mobile	Mobile	78-117
California	Los Angeles	Los Angeles	All ED's in Los Angeles County except 1-10 are Los Angeles City
	Oakland	Alameda	18-29, 38, 72-160, 207-213, 218
	San Francisco	San Francisco	1-315
Colorado	Denver	Denver	47-206
Connecticut	Bridgeport	Fairfield	3-57, 59-72, 92-102, 109-118, 600-601, 604, 607, 609
	Hartford	Hartford	154-207, 605, 606, 608
	New Haven	New Haven	319-327, 344-361, 372-443
	Waterbury	New Haven	462-494
Delaware	Wilmington	Newcastle	21-70
District of Columbia	Washington	No County	1-245
Florida	Jacksonville	Duval	60-67
Georgia	Atlanta	Fulton	42-104, 106, 110-135, 170-174
	Savannah	Chatham	33-77
Illinois	Chicago	Cook	140 to 1657, with gaps
	East St. Louis	St. Clair	102-140
	Peoria	Peoria	67-107, 158
	Springfield	Sangamon	116-157
Indiana	Evansville	Vanderburg	88-146
	Fort Wayne	Allen	28, 31-69
	Indianapolis	Marion	30-267, 269
	South Bend	St. Joseph	158-193
	Terre Haute	Vigo	134-173, 198-199
Iowa	Des Moines	Polk	120-171
Kansas	Kansas City	Wyandotte	146-208
	Wichita	Sedgwick	100-146, 80
Kentucky	Covington	Kenton	80-124
	Louisville	Jefferson	23-228
Louisiana	New Orleans	Orleans	1-248
Maine	Portland	Cumberland	61-100
Maryland	Baltimore	Baltimore City	1-405
Massachusetts	Boston	Suffolk	1254-1657, 1925, 1926, 1929, 1934, 1941, 1947, 1948, 1956
	Brockton	Plymouth	1178-1208, 1214, 1253
	Cambridge	Middlesex	742-790, 1932, 1939, 1940
	Fall River	Bristol	113-178, 1923
	Holyoke	Hampden	547-589, 662-674
	Lawrence	Essex	333-364, 1937
	Lowell	Middlesex	832-871, 1954
	Lynn	Essex	365-412, 1933, 1950
	New Bedford	Bristol	182-214
	Somerville	Middlesex	987-1021
	Springfield	Hampden	590-661
	Worcester	Worcester	1850-1922, 1946
Michigan	Detroit	Wayne	4-278, 319, 326, 324, 323
	Grand Rapids	Kent	50-109, 118-148, 182
	Saginaw	Saginaw	47-71, 134
Minnesota	Duluth	Saint Louis	144-196, 247, 248
	Minneapolis	Hennepin	17-212
	St. Paul	Ramsey	22-89, 108-136, 190-193
Missouri	Kansas City	Jackson	17-215
	St. Joseph	Buchanan	46-102, 163, 164
	St. Louis	St. Louis City	1-367, 388-481

43

STATE	CITY	COUNTY	ENUMERATION DISTRICTS
Nebraska	Omaha	Douglas	1-125
New Hampshire	Manchester	Hillsboro	122-171
New Jersey	Bayonne	Hudson	Not listed separately
	Camden	Camden	2-81, 104
	Elizabeth	Union	53-100, 155
	Hoboken	Hudson	43-77
	Jersey City	Hudson	78-228, 300
	Newark	Essex	1-144, 232-234, 236-238, 240, 242
	Passaic	Passaic	67-85, 104-110, 193
	Paterson	Passaic	86-158
	Trenton	Mercer	45-103, 105, 106, 126, 128
New York	Albany	Albany	1-162, 225, 226
	Buffalo	Erie	1-239, 310
	New York City		
	Manhattan	New York	1-1757, with gaps
	Bronx	New York	1397-1744, with gaps
	Brooklyn	Kings	1-761, 763-955
	Queens	Queens	1145-1290
	Richmond	Richmond	1291-1337
	Rochester	Monroe	39-98, 109-134, 146-213, 223-229
	Schenectady	Schenectady	174-224
	Syracuse	Onondaga	86-195
	Troy	Rensselaer	42-80
	Utica	Oneida	Not listed separately
	Yonkers	Westchester	138-189
Ohio	Akron	Summit	119-171
	Canton	Stark	Not listed separately
	Cincinnati	Hamilton	1-199, 372-375, 377, 378
	Cleveland	Cuyahoga	49-432, with gaps
	Columbus	Franklin	Not listed separately
	Dayton	Montgomery	48-125
	Toledo	Lucas	30-149
	Youngstown	Mahoning	Not listed separately
Oklahoma	Oklahoma City	Oklahoma	183, 200-229, 296
Oregon	Portland	Multnomah	124-210, 227-246, 321, 327, 329 (missing - 325, 329, 328, 330)
Pennsylvania	Allentown	Lehigh	131-177
	Altoona	Blair	34-60
	Erie	Erie	67-106, 192
	Harrisburg	Dauphin	51-94, 173
	Johnstown	Cambria	117-163
	Philadelphia	Philadelphia	1-1223
	Pittsburgh	Allegheny	248-657
	Reading	Berks	31-119
	Scranton	Lackawanna	53-136, 145-148
	Wilkes-Barre	Luzerne	Not listed separately
Rhode Island	Pawtucket	Providence	116-145
	Providence	Providence	146-273
South Carolina	Charleston	Charleston	18-65
Tennessee	Memphis	Shelby	95-285, 320-328
	Nashville	Davidson	12-98, 177
Texas	Dallas	Dallas	22-78, 186-187
	Fort Worth	Tarrant	108-155
	Houston	Harris	46-108
	San Antonio	Bexar	1-63
Utah	Salt Lake City	Salt Lake	95-96, 100-145, 239-231, 243
Virginia	Norfolk	Norfolk City	18-70, 79-81
	Richmond	Richmond City	63-145, 49-58
Washington	Seattle	King	58-224, 357, 361, 362
	Spokane	Spokane	145-206
	Tacoma	Pierce	213-284
Wisconsin	Milwaukee	Milwaukee	14-273, 297-311

CENSUS MICROFILM RENTAL PROGRAM
P.O. Box 30
Annapolis Junction, MD 20701-0030

 **ORDER FORM**

<table>
<tr><td rowspan="4">F
R
O
M</td><td colspan="3">LIBRARY</td></tr>
<tr><td colspan="3">STREET ADDRESS</td></tr>
<tr><td colspan="3">CITY, STATE, ZIP</td></tr>
<tr><td>ACCOUNT NO.</td><td>LIBRARY CONTACT PERSON</td><td>TELEPHONE NO.</td></tr>
</table>

- Payments accompanying orders should be made payable to Census Microfilm Rental Program

- Deposit Account Customers receive a $.05/per reel discount

- Please enter your orders carefully in the space provided below. Be sure that you have used the correct microfilm publication number and roll number as provided in the National Archives & Record Service Catalog.

PUBLICATION NO.	ROLL NO.	DATE WANTED IF OTHER THAN ASAP	LIBRARY COMMENTS

TOTAL ROLLS ORDERED	TOTAL ORDER AMOUNT	DATE ORDER MAILED	

THIS ORDER FORM MAY BE PHOTOCOPIED

CENSUS MICROFILM RENTAL PROGRAM
P.O. Box 30
Annapolis Junction, MD 20701-0030

ORDER FORM

LIBRARY		
STREET ADDRESS		
CITY, STATE, ZIP		
ACCOUNT NO.	LIBRARY CONTACT PERSON	TELEPHONE NO.

- **Payments accompanying orders should be made payable to Census Microfilm Rental Program**
- **Deposit Account Customers receive a $.05/per reel discount**
- **Please enter your orders carefully in the space provided below. Be sure that you have used the correct microfilm publication number and roll number as provided in the National Archives & Record Service Catalog.**

PUBLICATION NO.	ROLL NO.	DATE WANTED IF OTHER THAN ASAP	LIBRARY COMMENTS

TOTAL ROLLS ORDERED	TOTAL ORDER AMOUNT	DATE ORDER MAILED	

THIS ORDER FORM MAY BE PHOTOCOPIED

CENSUS MICROFILM RENTAL PROGRAM
P.O. Box 30
Annapolis Junction, MD 20701-0030

LIBRARY		
STREET ADDRESS		
CITY, STATE, ZIP		
ACCOUNT NO.	LIBRARY CONTACT PERSON	TELEPHONE NO.

- Payments accompanying orders should be made payable to Census Microfilm Rental Program

- Deposit Account Customers receive a $.05/per reel discount

- Please enter your orders carefully in the space provided below. Be sure that you have used the correct microfilm publication number and roll number as provided in the National Archives & Record Service Catalog.

PUBLICATION NO.	ROLL NO.	DATE WANTED IF OTHER THAN ASAP	LIBRARY COMMENTS

TOTAL ROLLS ORDERED	TOTAL ORDER AMOUNT	DATE ORDER MAILED	

THIS ORDER FORM MAY BE PHOTOCOPIED